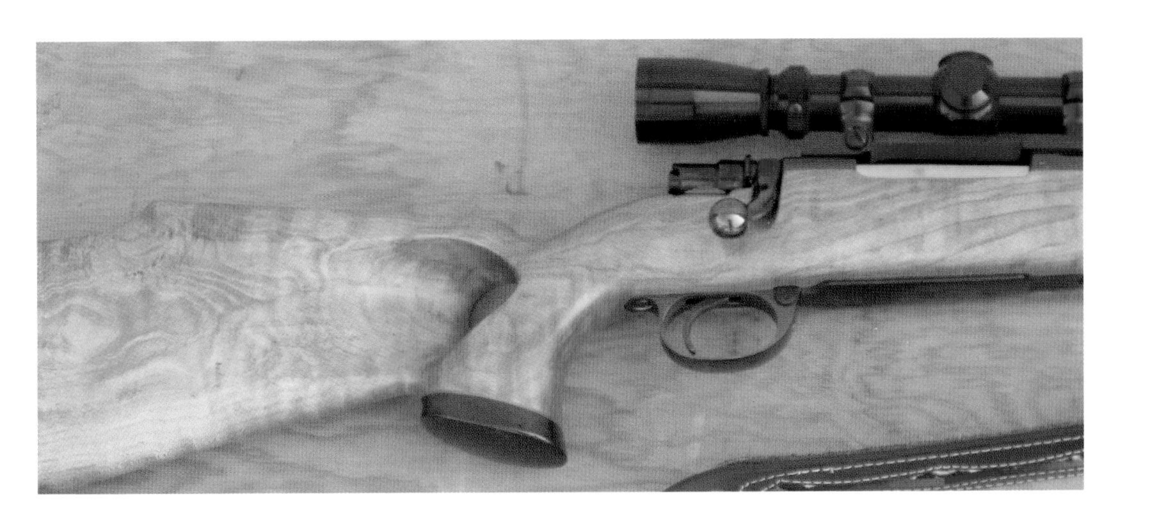

# ILLUSTRATED GUIDE to COMBAT WEAPONS

Madsen M5C
M1 Thompson .45
UZI 9mm
H/K MP5 9mm
Colt M16 9m

# ILLUSTRATED GUIDE to COMBAT WEAPONS

Jan Suermondt

Published 2004 by Grange Books
an imprint of Grange Books PLC.
The Grange
Kings North Industrial Estate
Hoo nr. Rochester
Kent, UK
ME3 9ND

www.grangebooks.co.uk

All enquiries please email info@grangebooks.co.uk



All notations of errors or omissions (author inquiries, permissions) concerning the content of this book should be addressed to:
TAJ Books 27, Ferndown Gardens, Cobham, Surrey, UK, KT11 2BH, info@tajbooks.com.

ISBN 1-84013-693-6

Printed in China.

1 2 3 4 5 08 07 06 05 04

# Introduction

The development of infantry weapons in use today extends, in many cases, as far back as the 1880s. Indeed, this period saw warfare transformed beyond recognition, and layed the foundations for most of the weapons in service around the world today.

The most serious threat likely to have been encountered by an infantryman in the 1880s would have been concentrated volley fire from well-drilled troops, armed with bolt-action rifles. The First World War saw the first large scale use of machine guns in the fire support role and the Second saw the widespread use of automatic weapons in the offensive role first at squad level with light machine guns and then, increasingly, on an individual basis with the proliferation of sub-machine guns and, later, more sophisticated assault rifles.

Technologically too this was a period of dramatic change, not only in the weapons themselves but also other areas of warfare. Advances in radio equipment enabled the execution of the closely integrated combined arms operations that were first demonstrated by the Germans with their Blitzkrieg tactics and later adopted by all sides to a lesser or greater extent. By the end of the war in Europe this had been developed to such a high degree by the Allies that forward observers could virtually snipe at enemy targets with long-range artillery and ground attack aircraft. This in turn meant that the infantryman was now in need of weapons to be able to defend himself against these threats rather than relying solely on anti tank and anti aircraft artillery. Several countries developed infantry anti-tank weapons such as the PIAT, Bazooka and Panzerfaust but only the Germans succeeded in developing a shoulder fired anti-aircraft weapon. Obviously with the almost total Allied air supremacy in Europe by the war's end there was a much greater incentive and rocket technology in Germany led the world as demonstrated by the V2. The weapon known as the Fliegerfaust was a multi-barelled device that fired a salvo of rockets into the path of a low flying aircraft, each warhead was equipped with a proximity fuse and was sufficient to bring down a fighter-bomber. How successful the weapon would have been remains unknown as the end of the war prevented it's introduction to service but it does none the less represent a milestone as the first shoulder fired surface to air missile.

The Second World War was, like no other, a war of industry. The development of many weapons during the war follows a path of simplification and adapting to speed production as it became apparent that far more weapons would be needed than any of the combatants realised when the war began. This race for production shows quite clearly in many of the weapons used during the war. Compare for example the pre-war US Thompson sub-machine gun with it's shaped wooden stock and handgrip and expensive and time consuming mechanism machined from solid metal with M3 sub-machine gun, designed for war and constructed largely from steel pressings, stamped out by the thousand in car factories.

Post-war the twentieth century saw a rapid development of infantry weapons, which shows little sign of slowing in the new millennium. This book offers an over view of combat weapon development; from rifles to rocket launchers and mortars. The basic mechanical principles of firearms have not changed greatly since World War I, but technology has inevitably had an impact on all aspects of weapon development. From manufacturing processes, and materials to developments in munitions there has been enormous change. It is likely that major technological advances will change the nature of small arms in more fundamental way in the near future. Heckler and Koch have already demonstrated their G11 rifle, which uses caseless ammunition - the propellant encases the bullet, and completely combusts on firing, meaning that no ejector system is necessary, resulting in an extremely high rate of fire. Electromagnetically propelled bullets are now being 'fired' soundlessly in experimental trials of 'rail guns', and man portable rocket systems, and smart munitions offer capabilities that only a short while ago were firmly in the realms of science fiction.

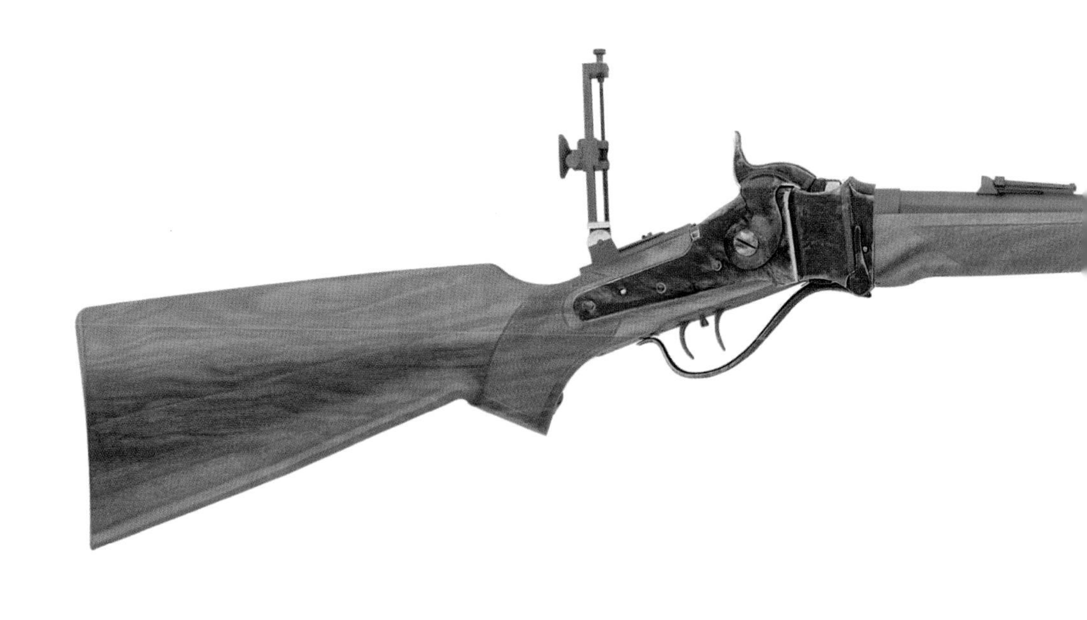

## 12.7mm Gepard M1, M1A1

Produced by Technika, the Gepard Ml is a single-shot anti-materiel rifle firing the Russian 12.7mm cartridge. The barrel is carried in a tubular cradle, which also mounts the bipod, and a barrel extension carries the padded butt plate. The pistol grip acts as the bolt handle. Aiming is done by means of a 12x telescope, and the weapon is sufficiently accurate to deliver a 300mm group at 600 meters range, at which distance the armour-piercing bullet will defeat 15mm of steel armour.The M1Al is the same weapon but mounted on a backpack frame that also serves as a firing mount for use in soft ground or snow; the bipod is still attached to the cradle but folded up when the frame is used. The M1A1 weighs an additional 6lb 10oz at 48lb 8oz (22kg).

CARTRIDGE
12.7 x 107mm Soviet

DIMENSIONS
Length o/a: 1570mm (61.81 in) Barrel: 1100mm (43.30in) Weight: 19.0kg (41lb 14oz) Rifling: 8 grooves, rh Magazine: none; single shot

IN PRODUCTION 1992-

## 12.7mm Gepard M2

The Gepard M2 is the automatic version of the M1 and operates on the long recoil system., the barrel recoiling inside a cylindrical jacket and receiver. A cylindrical cradle extends from the front of the receiver to support the barrel for most of its length.

A bipod is attached to the barrel jacket, and a telescope sight is standard. The magazine is mounted alongside the pistol grip and prevents the weapon from being fired by a left handed user. There is a manual safety-catch on left side of the receiver.

CARTRIDGE
12.7 x 107mm Soviet

DIMENSIONS (M2)
Length o/a: 1530mm (60.23in) Weight: 12.0kg (26lbs 7oz) Barrel: 1100mm (43.31in), Rifling: 8 grooves, rh Magazine: 5 or 10 rounds

IN PRODUCTION 1994-

*14.5mm Gepard M3 1*

## 14.5mm Gepard M3

This is effectively an enlarged version of the Gepard M2. Firing the powerful 14.5mm AP bullet, with a muzzle velocity of 3280 ft/sec (1000m/sec) it can penetrate 25mm of homogenous armour plate at 600 metres range and has a maximum range of well over 1000 metres. As it fires a more powerful round than the M2 the M3 is fitted with a hydro-pneumatic recoil system and a more effective muzzle brake to counter the increased recoil. There is a manual safety catch on the left side of the receiver.

CARTRIDGE
14.5 x 114mm Soviet

DIMENSIONS
Length o/a: 1880mm (74.0in) Barrel: 1480mm (58.27in) Weight: 20.0kg (44lbs 1oz} Rifling: 8 grooves, rh Magazine: 5 or 10 rounds

IN PRODUCTION 1995-

## 57mm M18

There are three basic models of this weapon, the M18, M18A1, and the T1SE16. These can be fired from the ground, shoulder or from a M74 or M 191 7 A2 mount. The complete weapon consists of the barrel group, breech mechanism group, a firing cable group, trigger mechanism group, bipod assembly and an extendable handle assembly. The M18 and M18A1 have their chamber and breechblock handles located in different positions. The M18 has its one the left and the M18A1 is on the right. The major difference between the M 18A1 and the T15E16 is in the linkage between the trigger mechanism group and the breech mechanism group. The following types of ammunition are available: HE, HEAT, canister, WP and TP. Its effective range in the anti-tank role is approx 400m and its maximum range, at 39 degrees elevation, with a HEAT round is 4,000m. It is provided with an M86F (M86CI telescope which has '17" field of view and a magnification of x2.8. The M18 is built in Communist China under the designation Type 36.

Calibre: 57mm
Length: 156,2cm
Length of barrel: 122cm Weight: 18.2kg
Range: 400m (effective) 4000m (max)
Crew: 1 -2

## 89mm STRIM

This weapon has been developed by Luchaire SA and is manufactured in cooperation with the Manufacture Nationale d' Armes de Saint-Etienne, and is marketed by Hotchkiss-Brandt. The rocket launcher itself is of glass fibre construction and is reusable. When required for action a rocket in its container is attached to the rear of the launcher, as this is done the firing circuit is connected. The rocket is kept in a sealed container which is 62.6cm in length and weighs a total of 3.2kg. The rocket itself weighs 2.2kg and has a shaped charge warhead 80mm in diameter. The rocket has a muzzle velocity of 300m/s and will, according to the manufacture penetrate 400mm of armour or concrete. As the rocket leaves the launcher nine stabilisers unfold and these stabilise the rocket in flight. Flight time to 330m = 1.25sec and flight time to 360m= 1.36 sec. The STRIM is fitted with the APX M 290 sighting system which is graduated from 0 to 1,000m, a passive telescope for night action is also available. Other rockets available apart from the basic anti-tank model, are a practice rocket, an illuminating rocket, an incendiary rocket and the AVL light anti-tank rocket.

Calibre: 88,9mm
Length: 116.8cm (carrying), 160cm (ready for action)
Weight: 4.5kg (carrying including telescope), 7.3kg (ready for action)
Range: 200-600m (practical) 2,300m (max at 45° angle)
Crew: 2

*AAT-F1*

## MAS AAT 52 France

developed as a direct result of French experience in Indo-China in the early 1950s. The French army was, at the time, equipped with a variety of machine guns of British, German and American origin. The proliferation of weapon and ammunition types proved a logistical nightmare, and plans were put in hand to develop an indigenously produced replacement. The result was the AA 52, designed from the outset for ease of production, maximum use has been made of steel pressings and welded fabrication. Operation is by delayed blow back, using a two-piece bolt similar to that of the FA MAS rifle, in which the light forward part of the bolt has to overcome the inertia of the heavy rear section before the breech can be opened. The chamber is fluted so as to float the case on a layer of gas to ease extraction, and fired cartridges are easily recognised by the longitudinal scoring. Over the years the gun has proved to be reliable and efficient and has also been put into service by several former French colonies.

CARTRIDGE
7.5 x 54 French Service
7.62 x 51mm NATO

DIMENSIONS
Length o/a: 990mm (38.9in) Weight: 9.88kg (21lb 13oz) Barrel: 488mm (19.2in) Rifling: 4 grooves, rh
Feed system: 50-round belt Rate of fire: 700 rds/min

IN PRODUCTION 1952-

*AK 47*

## AK 47 SERIES

The AK47 in all its numerous versions is probably the most widely used weapon in the world. Originally designed by Mikhail Kalashnikov it first entered service with the Russian army in 1951. The basic design has been subject to numerous modifications and has been copied in both its original and modified forms all over the world. But no matter how they vary, the basic structure remains the same and is always recognisable. The various versions turned out by other countries are usually distinguished by personal preference - handgrips, different styles of butt, grenade launching attachments and so forth, but the basic Kalashnikov can always be seen in the receiver and the safety lever. Larger differences may appear when the principle is applied to a new' design, for example the Galil, R4 and Finnish models.

CARTRIDGE AK-47
7.62mm x 39mm Soviet M1943

DIMENSIONS AK-47
Length, stock extended: 869mm (34.21in)
Length, stock folded 699mm (27.52in)
Weight: 4.30kg (9lb 8oz)Barrel: 414mm (16.3in)Rifling 4grooves, rh
Magazine capacity: 30 rounds
Rate of fire: 600 rds/min

IN PRODUCTION 1949-

*AK 47*

*AKSU 74*

## AKSU 74

This weapon first saw action in Afghanistan in 1982. It is simply a shortened version of the standard AK 74 rifle, intended for use by armoured troops, special forces and others requiring a more compact weapon. There is a muzzle attachment that compensates for firing a rifle cartridge in a much shorter barrel than that for which it was originally designed. The design has been copied in Yugoslavia, though chambered for the 5.56mm NATO cartridge.

CARTRIDGE
5.45mm x 39.5mm Soviet

DIMENSIONS
Length, stock extended: 730mm (28.75in)
Length, stock folded: 490mm (19.3in)
Weight: 2.7kg (5lb 15oz)Barrel: 206.5mm (8.13in)Rifling: 4 grooves, rh
Magazine capacity: 30 rounds
Rate of fire: 700 rds/min

IN PRODUCTION 1975

*APS Underwater Rifle*

## APS UNDERWATER RIFLE

mechanism, with the gas cylinder above the barrel. It has a unique deeply curved magazine, a pistol grip, folding butt, and facility for selective fire. The APS has a muzzle velocity of 1198 ft/sec (365 m/sec) in air.

Cartridge
5.66mm MPS

DIMENSIONS
Length, butt extended: 33.07in (840mm) Length, butt folded: 24.17in (614mm)
Weight: 5lb 5oz (24.0kg)
Barrel: n/a
Magazine: 26-round box
Cyclic rate. n/a

IN PRODUCTION -

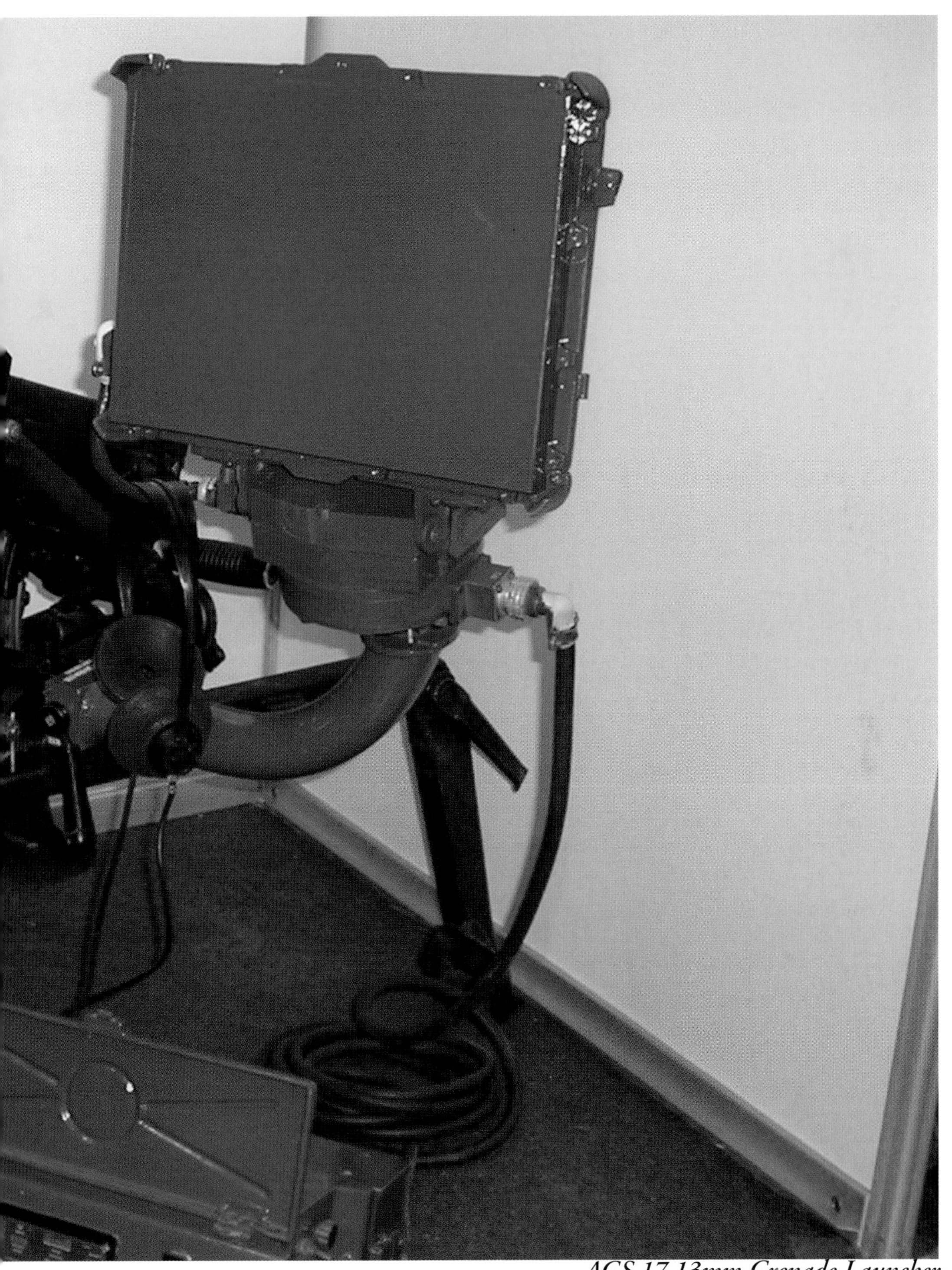

*AGS 17 13mm Grenade Launcher*

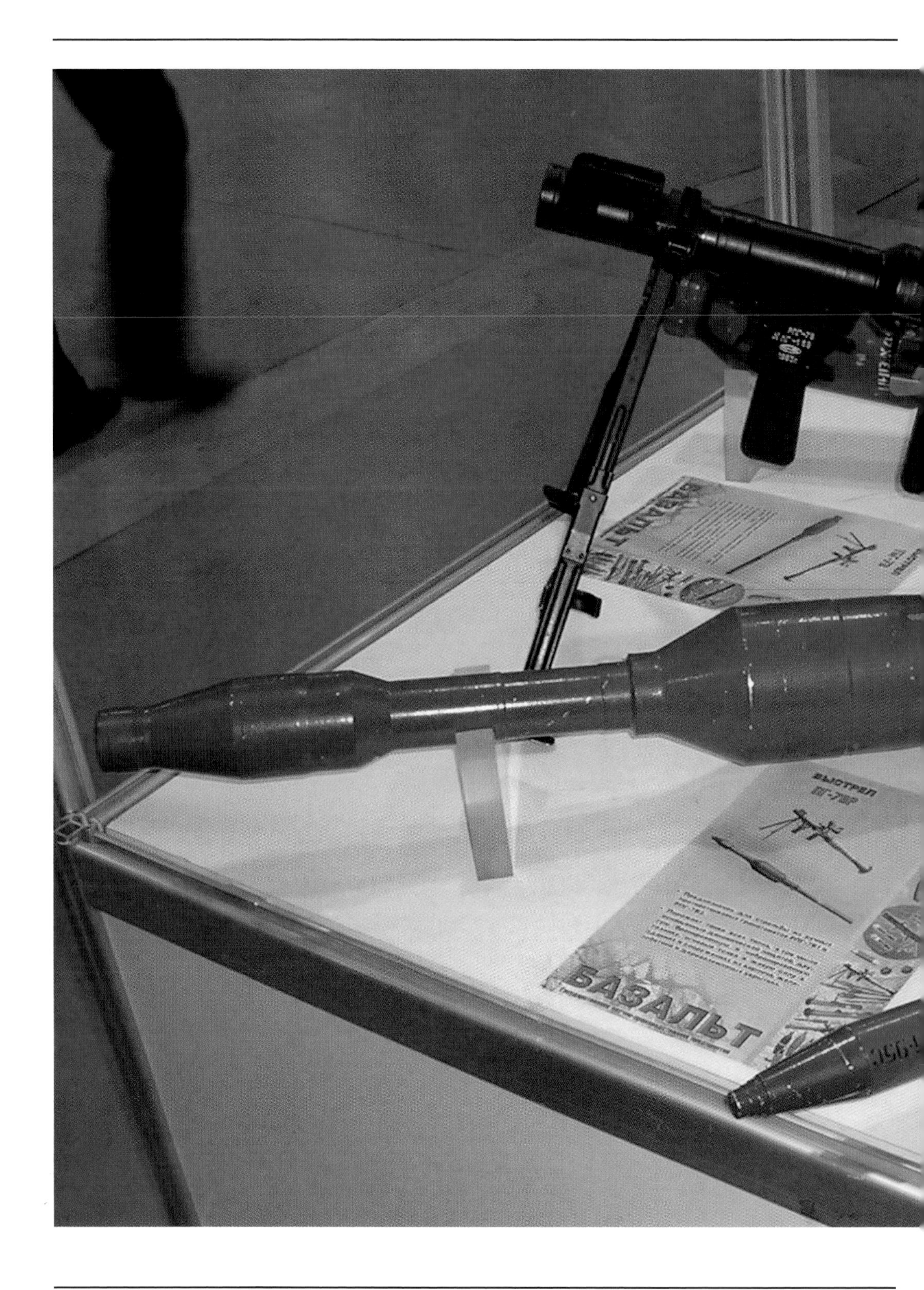
ВЫСТРЕЛ
БАЗАЛЬТ

*RPG-7V Grenade Launcher with FAE and FRAG rounds*

*AS-94*

## AS-94 RIFLE RUSSIA

The AS94 is a gas-operated weapon. Its receiver is similar in design to the Kalashnikov series of rifles, but the gas cylinder has been relocated to the underside of the barrel. The gun is furnished with an L-shaped butt, and pistol grip; and ammunition is fed from a curved magazine. There is a selective fire mechanism that permits the fire of two-round bursts.

Cartridge: 5.45 x 39.5mm
Length: 37.12in (943mm)
Weight: 81b 8oz (3.85kg)
Barrel: n/a
Magazine: 30-round box
Muzzle velocity: CQ 2952 ft/sec (900 m/sec)
Cyclic rate: 600 rds/min
Manufacturer: Izhmash

*Accuracy International L96A1*

## Accuracy International L96A1

sniping rifle of the British Army by the L96A1. The Accuracy International L96A1 is the first purpose made sniper rifle to be used by UK forces, all previous weapons being conversions of standard service rifles. The L96A1 owes more to target shooting practices than military rifle design. In its civilian guise, prior to adoption by the military, it was known as the Accuracy International Model PM, a target weapon designed by target shooting Olympic gold medallist, Malcolm Cooper. Although conventional in appearance the weapon is actually of quite unusual construction. The heavy stainless steel barrel is secured to an aluminium chassis and does not touch the plastic fore-end at any point. The chassis also supports the stock, butt, action and bipod, and the plastic furniture merely provides a protective outer casing. First deliveries were in 1986 since when over 1200 have been supplied to the British army.

CARTRIDGE 7.62 x 51mm NATO

DIMENSIONS
Length o/a- 1124mm (44.25in) Weight: 6.50kg (14lb 5oz) Barrel- 654mm (25.75in) Rifling- 4 grooves, rh Magazine capacity- 10 rounds

IN PRODUCTION 1985 -

*CETME Ameli 5.56mm Spain*

## CETME Ameli 5.56mm Spain

Military Materiel) the Ameli was produced by Empresa National Santa Barbara de Industrias Militares (the national arsenal organisation), which is now a subsidiary of General Dynamics. Although the Ameli bears a striking resemblance MG42 it is in fact a completely new weapon. It uses the same Heckler & Koch type roller-locked, delayed blow back mechanism as the CETME Model L rifle and indeed several of the parts are interchangeable with the Model L. The Ameli can be used on its bipod for squad support or on a tripod for sustained fire, having a quick-change barrel. It has been adopted by the Spanish Army and is one of the best 5.56mm light machine guns currently on offer.

CARTRIDGE 5.56 x 45mm NATO

DIMENSIONS
Length o/a: 970mm (38.2in) Weight: 635kg (14lb 0oz) Barrel: 400mm (15.75in) Rifling: 6 grooves, rh
Feed system: belt
Rate of fire: 850 or 1200 rds/min

IN PRODUCTION 1982-

## Australia Austen SMG

Designed in 1941 the Austen, from' Australian Sten' was intended as a replacement for the earlier Owen. The barrel, body and trigger mechanism of the Mark 2 Sten were copied, but the bolt mechanism was copied from the German MP38, as was the buttstock but with a slight alteration to the locking system. The magazine was also basically Sten, though of a smaller capacity. A front pistol grip was a useful addition. The Austen was never popular and the Australian soldiers preferred the Owen gun. Although specifically intended for mass production, no more than about 20,000 were manufactured between mid-1942 and early 1945. In 1944 an improved version was designed; this was called the Mark 2, but the differences between it and the Mark 1 are so radical that it could well have been given a different name.

Calibre 9mm
Length 33.25in
Weight 8lb 12oz
Barrel 7.75in long, 6 grooves, right hand twist
Feed system 2B-round detachable box magazine
System of operation Blow back, selective fire
Rate of fire (cyclic) 500rpm
Manufacturers
Diecasters Ltd., Melbourne
W. J. Carmichael & Co., Melbourne

## Australia Owen SMG

The Owen gun was the principal sub-machine gun of the Australian Army in World War 2. It was designed in 1940 by Lieutenant Evelyn Owen produced the prototype of the Owen gun in 1940. Pre-production models in a variety of calibres were made for troop trials, and on 20 November 1941 the 9mm version was authorised for production and issue. Over 45,000 of the Mark 1 model were made before production ceased in September 1944. The most prominent feature of the Owen was the top-mounted magazine. This configuration was less cumbersome in practice, than it might appear, and it also allowed the assistance of gravity to promote a reliable feed. The magazine was a two-column type, much easier to fill than that of the Sten, and had the ejector machined as an integral part of the magazine mouth. Manufacture was by traditional methods of machining, which led to production figures being modest, and the gun is generally agreed to be unnecessarily heavy.

Calibre 9mm
Length 32.0in
Weight 91b 5oz
Barrel 9.75in long, 7 grooves, right hand twist
Feed system 33-round detachable box magazine
System of operation Blow back
Rate of fire (cyclic) 700rpm
Manufacturer Lysaght's Pty, Port Kemble,

*2.36 inch anti-tank, M1 (Bazooka)*

## BAZOOKA

Perhaps one of the most famous weapons ever made, development of the 'Bazooka' began in 1941, spurred on by America's entry into the war. A rocket propelled, hollow charge weapon, the 2.36in launcher came into service in 1942 in time to be used by the US troops in North Africa. At that time one of America's favourite comedians was a Mr. Bob Burns, and one of his props was a complex and fearful wind instrument of his own invention which he called his 'Bazooka'. The similarity between this and the long pipe of the 2.36in launcher caught the fancy of some unsung GI, and ever since, shoulder-fired rocket launchers have been called 'Bazookas'.

A larger version, of 3.45in calibre, was developed towards the end of the war, but since the 2.36in appeared to be capable of doing all that was needed, the 'Super Bazooka' was shelved, and it was not put into production until 1951, when the appearance of the Russian T -34 tank in Korea rendered the 2.36in model obsolete over-night.

Calibre 2.36in
Length 54in
Weight 13.25lb
Barrel Smoothbore
Firing system Electric; 2 dry batteries in pistol grip
Projectile & weight HEAT 3.4lb Rocket
Maximum range 400yds
Muzzle velocity 300ft/sec
Penetration ca 80mm

*BXP*

## BXP

The BXP is South African design, used by their army and police. The BXP is a versatile weapon that can be fitted with a silencer, a grenade launching attachment, or various types of muzzle compensator. It is made from steel pressings, and the bolt is hollowed out to wrap around that portion of the barrel that is inside the receiver, so that it has a full-length barrel even though only a part of it is visible.

CARTRIDGE 9mm Parabellum

DIMENSIONS
Length, stock extended: 607mm (23.9in)
Length, stock folded: 387mm (15.24in)
Barrel: 208mm (8.19in) Weight, empty: 250kg (51b 8oz)
Rifling: 6 grooves, rh Magazine capacity: 22 or 32 rounds
Rate of fire: 1000 rds/min

IN PRODUCTION 1988

*Barrett Light Fifty M82A1*

## BARRETT LIGHT FIFTY M82A1

Firing a 12.7mm round the Barret M82A1, also known as the Light Fifty, was one of the first heavy sniping rifles to achieve success. It is a recoil-operated, semi-automatic with a rotating bolt. The fluted barrel is equipped with a large muzzle brake, and the telescope sight and adjustable butt are fitted as standard. The Barrett has been adopted by several military and police forces as an anti-material sniping weapon and also for detonating explosive devices at a safe distance. The M82A1 performed well during Operation Desert Storm in the 1991 Gulf War, when US ground troops used it successfully against APCs and high value personnel.

CARTRIDGE
12.7 x 99 (50 Browning)

DIMENSIONS
Length: o/a 1549mm (61.0in) Weight: 12.90kg (28lb 6oz) Barrel: 737mm (29.0in) Rifling: 12 grooves, rh Magazine capacity: 11 rounds Rate of fire: semi-automatic only

IN PRODUCTION 1983-92

*Barrett M82A2*

## BARRETT M82A2 AND M95

In 1992 a major redesign of the Light Fifty took place in an attempt to make the weapon less cumbersome. In order to reduce the overall length without adversely effecting performance the design was reworked to a bullpup layout, in which the action and barrel are placed further back in the stock so as to retain the same length of barrel but in a lesser overall length. This places the receiver and action alongside the firer's face and the magazine now lies behind the pistol grip and trigger. The result was the M82A2 with a reduction in overall length of 5.5inches and a weight saving of 1lb 6oz this is proving just as successful as its forebear.
The latest development of the Barret is the M95, a bolt action derivative of the M82A2.This offers a further reduction in both length and weight and an effective range of over 2000 yards.

CARTRIDGE
12.7 x 99mm (.50 Browning)

DIMENSIONS M82A2
Length: o/a 1409mm (55.5in) Weight: 12.24kg (27lb 0oz) Barrel: 737mm (29.0in) Rifling: 12 grooves, rh Magazine capacity: 11 rounds Rate of fire: semi-automatic only

IN PRODUCTION 1992 –1998

DIMENSIONS M95
Length: o/a 1143mm (45in) Weight: 11.2kg (24.7lb 0oz) Barrel: 737mm (29.0in) Rifling: 12 grooves, rh Magazine capacity: 5 rounds Rate of fire: bolt action

*Beretta Model 12s*

## BERETTA MODEL 12

The Model 12 is considerably different to earlier Beretta submachine guns, due to the retirement of the designer Marengoni in 1956 and the appearance of a new designer, Salza. It is primarily made of metal stampings and uses an overhung bolt that wraps around the barrel to reduce the length of the weapon. It has a front hand-grip and the stock may be a hinged, tubular metal type folding around to the right side of the weapon, or a detachable wooden type. The Italian forces adopted the Model12 in 1961 as did various South American and African countries. It has also been made under licence in Brazil and Indonesia.

CARTRIDGE 9mm Parabellum

DIMENSIONS
Length, stock extended: 645mm (25.4in)
Length, stock retracted: 418mm (16.45in)
Barrel: 200mm (7.87in) Weight, empty: 3.0kg (61b 10oz)
Rifling: 6 grooves, rh Magazine capacity: 20, 30, 40 rounds
Rate of fire: 550 rds/min

IN PRODUCTION 1959-78

*Blowpipe*

## Blowpipe and Javelin

14 armed forces in 10 countries. The system worked well in the 1982 Falklands War; both sides deployed it and several successes were recorded. It has also found its way to Afghanistan, and has been reported as being used by the Mujahideen from 1983 onwards. The basic Blowpipe comprises of two units. The first is the sealed launch canister containing the missile; the second is the aiming unit, a self-contained pack. To prepare for action the aiming unit is clipped to the launch canister and put on the firer's shoulder. When the operator has acquired the target and confirmed it as hostile he pulls the trigger, generating a current that energises the thermal battery. This powers up the aiming unit and one second later the missile fires. The missile is ejected from the launch tube by the first stage motor and, when well clear of the operator, the second stage ignites. The operator 'gathers' the missile and guides it onto the target using a thumb stick, which transmits signals by a radio link to the missile.

The latest version is the Javelin this uses the Blowpipe missile but with a more powerful motor, and the guidance system is a semi-automatic command line of sight (SACOS) unit in which all the operator needs to do is keep the cross-hairs on target. A TV camera in the aiming unit tracks a flare in the missile's tail and compares this with the information from the sight; any mismatch is converted into a correction signal, which is transmitted to the missile.

Origin: UK
Type: Surface to air missile (SAM)
Canister: length 54.7in (1390mm) weight 48.31 lb (29.1kg)
Missile: length 54.7in (1390mm) diameter 3in (76mm)
Propulsion: two-stage, solid fuel rocket motor
Effective range: 3 to 3.7 miles (5-6km)
Flight speed: Mach 1 plus

*Bofors AKS*

## Bofors AKS

Comprehensive series of trials in the mid-1980s. Changes were made to the butt, rear sights, cocking handle, bolt, selector switch, trigger guard and sling swivels largely in order to better withstand extreme cold conditions and be more easily operated by gloved hands. The metal is finished in a green enamel, to protect the steel against corrosion and aid concealment.
There are three variants of the CGA 5:-

CGA 5 (Ak5B)
This is the basic CGA 5 fitted with the British SUSAT (Sight Unit, Small Arms, Trilux) optical sight, there are no iron sights.

CGA 5D
This is the CGA 5 with iron sights and a Picatinny Rail sight mount.

CGA 5-C2
This is the short version of the standard CGA 5 for use by vehicle crew-men and others requiring a carbine.

CARTRIDGE
5.56 x 45mm NATO

DIMENSIONS
Length stock extended o/a: 1008mm (39.70in) Weight: 3.90kg (8lb 10oz) Barrel: 450mm (17.71in) Rifling: 6 grooves, rh Magazine capacity: 30 rounds Rate of fire: 650rds/min

IN PRODUCTION 1984-

*Boys Anti-tank Rifle*

## Boys Anti-tank Rifle

Entering service on 24 November 1937, the 'Boys Rifle', was probably the best of its class at the time. Firing a steel-cored bullet at 3250ft/sec it could penetrate any current tank at 250 yards. The recoil of the heavy cartridge was considerable, and the gun was fitted with a muzzle brake and allowed to recoil in a cradle mounting against a powerful buffer spring. A mono pod acted as front support, and the butt was thickly padded with rubber. The Boys saw action in France, Norway and the Far East, but it was rarely entirely successful. It was rarely seen after 1941, being replaced by less conventional but more effective weapons.

Variant
Rifle, Boys, Mark 2 Approved on 4 July 1942 this version had a barrel 4.5in shorter than the Mark 1, with certain unstressed components of aluminium and the butt pad stuffed with feathers, all in an endeavor to produce a lighter model for use by Airborne troops. Although approved, it was never taken into action; shortening the barrel had reduced the velocity and penetration, and by the time the Airborne troops went into action they had been provided with something better .

Calibre O.55in
Length 63.5in
Weight 36lb
Barrel 36in long, 7 grooves, right hand twist
Feed system 5-round, top-mounted, detachable box magazine
System of operation Bolt action
Muzzle velocity 3250ft/sec
Penetration 20mm/500m/0 degrees
Manufacturer Royal Small Arms Factory, Enfield Lock

## Brandt Mortier MO-120-RT-61

In France, the Brandt company produces conventional light and medium mortars in 60 and 81.4mm calibres, but as an organisation it is best known for its 120mm heavy mortars. It is in this calibre that the mortar can become a highly versatile adjunct to conventional artillery, and many armies use 120mm mortars in place of artillery. The smooth-bore models In this range are conventional mortars that can be used in exactly the same way as smaller-calibre models, but the rifled mortars are much more complex and in many ways resemble conventional high-angle guns. The rifled weapons fire pre-rifled projectiles whose range can be enhanced by the use of an auxiliary rocket unit that cuts in only when the bomb is at the top of its trajectory. A typical range with this rocket assistance is 13000 m (14,215 yards) for an HE bomb weighing 18.7 kg (41.23 lb). Despite their size and weight, the Brandt rifled mortars can thus have a very useful performance, and key weapons on the series include the Mortier MO-120-60 light mortar, Mortier MO-120-M65 strengthened mortar, Mortier MO-120-AM 50 heavy mortar, Mortier MO-120-LT mortar and Mortier MO-120-RT-61 rifled mortar.

Calibre: 120-mm (4.72in)
Length: barrel 2080 mm (81.9 in) Weights: mortar 582 kg (1,283 lb)HE bomb:18.7kg (41.23lb)
Maximum range: 13000 m (14,215yds) with rocket-assisted bomb

## Breda M1937

The Breda 37 was a final prewar attempt to produce a reasonably satisfactory medium machine gun for the Italian Army, it was certainly an improvement on earlier designs and was well liked by its users as a reliable weapon.
The mechanism is a simple gas piston type, but no opportunity was taken to design it so that the bolt began opening by a slow movement to start the empty case out of the chamber. The same violent operation as every other Italian gun occurred, which, inevitably, led to extraction problems and equally inevitably to oiled cartridges and all their associated problems.
The design of the rest of the gun was straightforward enough, and it was mounted on a simple and robust tripod, unfortunately it was fitted with an unnecessarily complicated feed system although this was later reoplaced in the 1938 model.

Variant
Model 1938
This changed the feed system to use a twenty-round detachable box mounted on top of the gun. A pistol grip at the rear end replaced the spade grips of the Model 37, but beyond that there was no other change. It appears that few of this model were made.

Calibre 8 mm
length 50.06in
Weight 43lb
Barrel 26.75in long, 4 grooves, right hand twist
Feed system 20-round strip
System of operation
Gas; vertical sliding lock
Rate of fire (cyclic) 450rpm
Manufacturer
Ernesto Breda SA, Turin

*Bren MK1*

## Bren MK1

The Bren Gun was evolved from the Czechoslovak ZB vz 26 light machine-gun. In 1930 there began a series of trials involving several designs, among them the vz 26 in the form of a slightly revised model, the vz 27.

The vz 27 emerged as a clear winner from these trials. However, it was made only in 7.92mm (.312in) calibre, and the British army wanted to retain the .303in (7.7mm) cartridge with its outdated cordite propellant and its awkward rimmed case.

Thus started a series of development models that involved the vz 27, the later vz 30 and eventually an interim model, the vz 32.

Then came the vz 33, and it was from this that the Royal Small Arms Factory at Enfield Lock evolved the prototype of what became the Bren Gun (Bren from the 'Br' of Brno, the place of origin, and the 'en' of Enfield Lock). Tooling up at Enfield lock resulted in the completion in 1937 of the first production Bren Gun Mk 1, and thereafter the type remained in production at Enfield and elsewhere until well after 1945 By 1940 well over 30,000 Bren Guns had been produced and the type was firmly established in service.

The Bren Gun was a superb light machine-gun. It was robust, reliable, easy to handle and to maintain, and it was not too heavy for its role It was also very accurate. After 1945 the type remained in service and remained for many yearsl in limited service with some armies as the Bren Gun L4 series. This version was modified to fire the NATO standard 7.62-mm (0.3-in) cartridge through a barrel chrome-plated to reduce wear.

Calibre .303in
Length 45.25in
Weight 22lb 5oz
Barrel 25.0in long, 6 grooves, right hand twist
Feed system 30-round, curved, detachable box magazine
System of operation
Gas; tipping bolt
Rate of fire (cyclic) 500rpm
Manufacturer Royal Small Arms Factory, Enfield Lock, Middlesex

*British 51mm Mortar*

## British 51mm Mortar

The British 51-mm Mortar was developed as successor to the 2in (51mm) mortar designed before World War II. Work on the new weapon started in the early 1970s mainly by the RARDE (Royal Armament Research and Development Establishment) at Fort Halstead in Kent. The 51mm is used by the British army at platoon level. In its production form the weapon outwardly resembles one of the many commando-type mortars in use elsewhere, but it is more complex. It consists mainly of a barrel and base-plate, but the design detail is quite involved. The mortar uses a lanyard-operated trigger mechanism, and aiming is assisted by a complex sight with an inbuilt Trilux illuminating source for use at night. The mortar was designed for really close-range operations at ranges as close as 50m (55yds), and this is achieved by the use of a short-range insert (SRI). In use the SRI is inserted in the base of the barrel to serve as a firing pin extension while at the same time allowing propellant gases to expand around the SRI to produce lower barrel pressures and thus decrease muzzle velocity and range. The normal minimum range is 150m (165yds), while the maximum is 800m (875yds) The mortar can be carried by one man, ammunition is carried in canvas and webbing satchels, and a webbing wallet is used to carry cleaning rods and a few ancillary equipment items. The ammunition range includes HE, illuminating and smoke bombs. The HE bomb contains a wall liner of pre-notched wire for anti-personnel use.

Calibre: 51mm (2in) Length: 750 mm (29.53 in)
Weights: mortar 6.28 kg (13.84lb)
HE bomb 0.92 kg (2.03lbl)Illuminating bomb 0.8 kg (1.76lb)Smoke bomb 0.9 kg (1.98 lb)
Maximum range: 800m (875 yds)

*Browning 0.5in M2*

## BROWNING 0.5IN M2

First produced in 1921, the 0.5in (12.7-mm) Browning heavy machine-gun is one of the most fearesome anti personnel weapons ever made. The projectile fired by the type is a prodigious man-stopper, and the machine-gun can also be used to defeat vehicles and light armour, especially when firing armour-piercing rounds. From the original Browning M1921 heavy machine-gun evolved a whole string of variants based on what was to become known as the M2

On all these variants the gun mechanism remained the same, being very similar to that used on the smaller M1917 machine-gun. Where the variants differed from each other was in the type of barrel fitted and the fixtures used to mount the gun.

One of the most numerous of the M2s has been the M2HB, the suffix denoting the Heavy Barrel. The HB version can be used in all manner of installations, and in the past has been employed as an infantry gun, as an anti-aircraft gun and also as a fixed and trainable aircraft gun. For infantry use the M2HB is usually mounted on a heavy tripod, but it can also be used mounted on vehicle pintles, ring mountings and pivots. Other M2s have included versions with water-cooled barrels, usually employed as anti-aircraft weapons, especially on US Navy vessels on which in World War II they were often fixed in multiple mountings for use against low-flying attack aircraft.

Single water-cooled mountings were often used to provide anti-aircraft defence for shore installations.

Calibre: 0.5in (12.7mm)
Length overall: 1654 mm (65.1in)
Length of barrel: 1143 mm (45 in)
Weights: gun 381 kg (84Ib) and tripod 19.96 kg (44lb) for M3 type
Rate of fire, cyclic: 450-575 rpm
Feed: 110 round metal-IInk belt

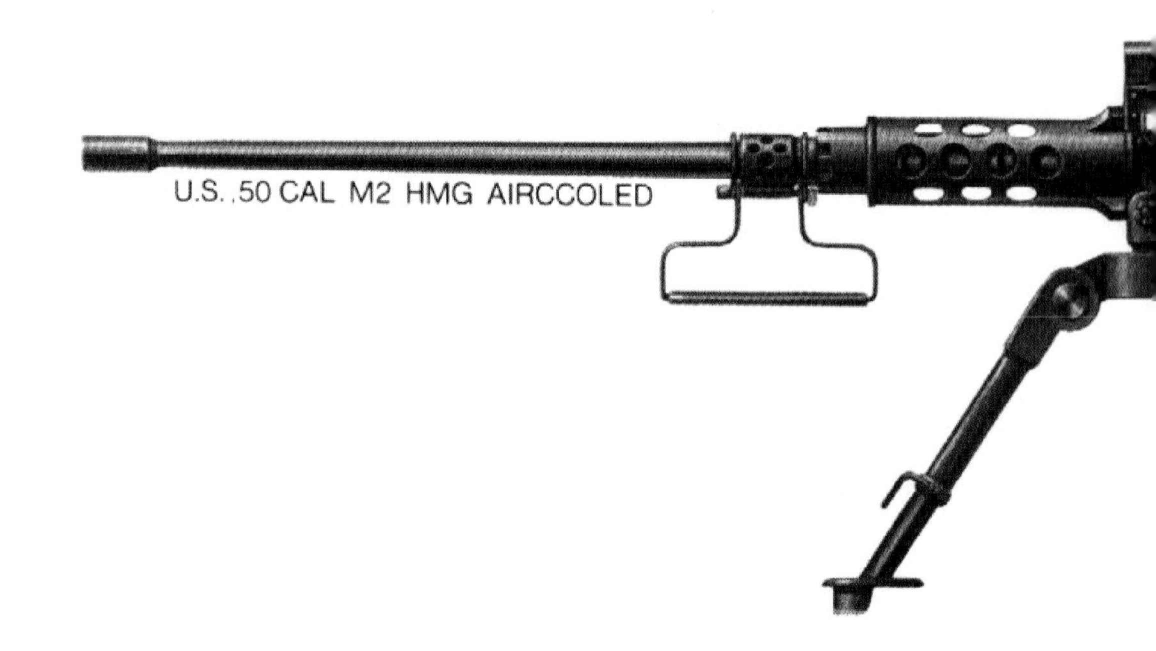


*Browning M2*

*Browning M1919*

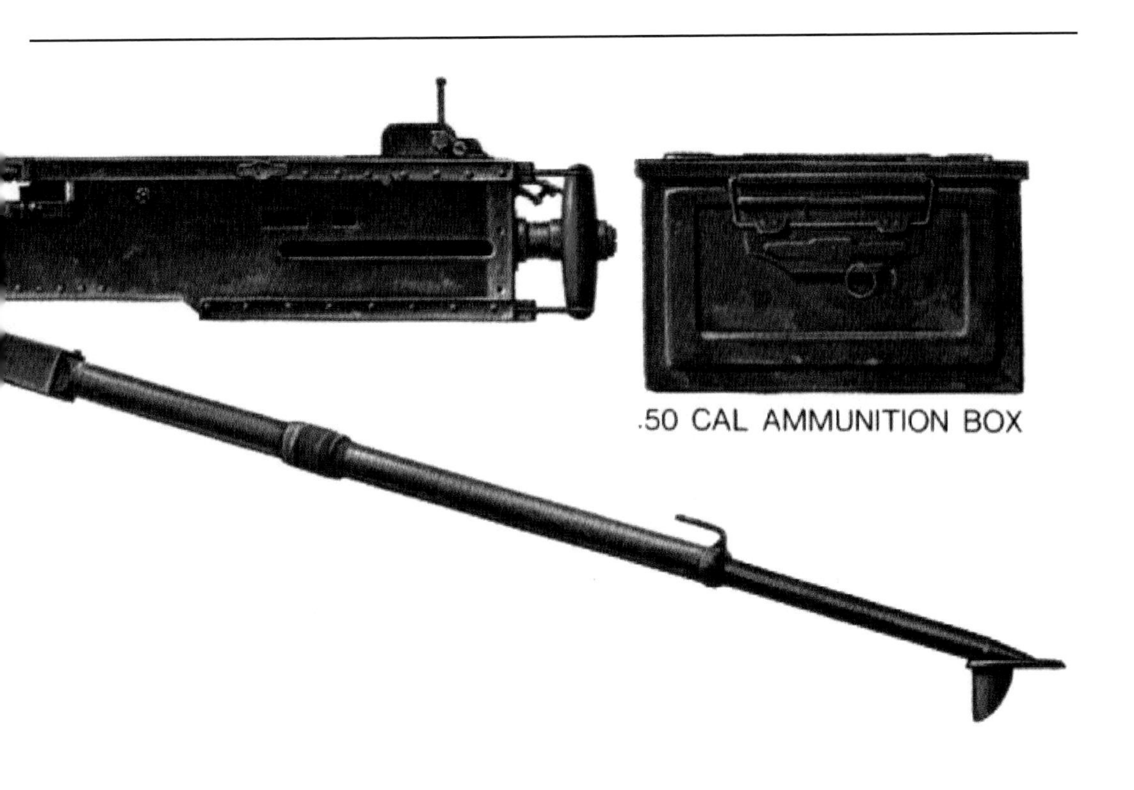

.50 CAL AMMUNITION BOX

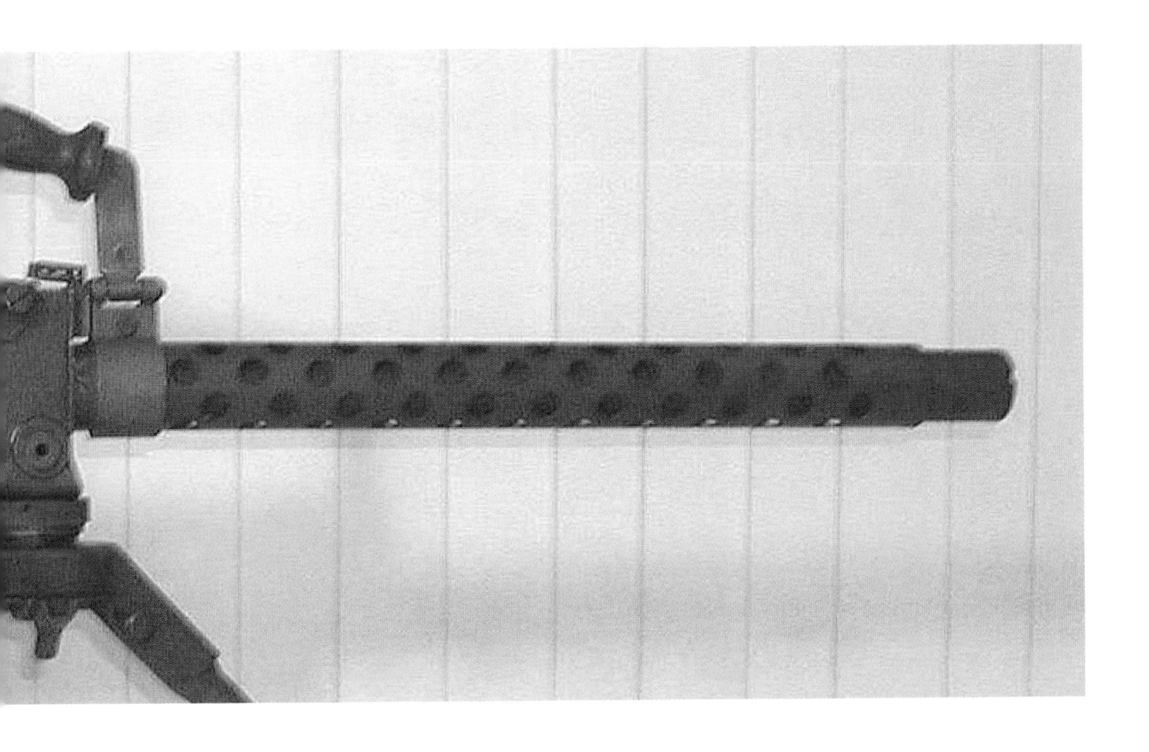

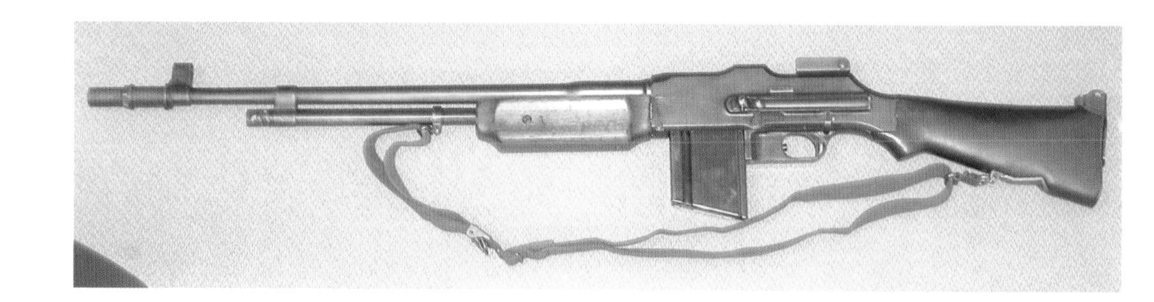

*Browning automatic rifle, M1918*

## Browning M1918

First issued to US forces in the summer of 1918, the Browning automatic rifle, M1918 remained the squad light automatic of the US Army from then until after World War II.

It was originally intended to be used during the assault, firing from the hip, a French theory for giving covering fire while crossing no-man's-land which, along with a lot of other peculiar French theories, was adopted by the US Army. But the action of the weapon is so violent that accurate fire under these conditions is almost impossible, and the gun was later provided with a bipod so that it could be used in the more conventional prone position. Another drawback was the bottom-mounted 20-round magazine, inconvenient to change in action and with a limited capacity for automatic fire. In spite of all this, however, it had the advantage of being designed with mass-production in mind, and it was relatively easy to produce.

As well as being standard in the US Army it was widely adopted by other countries as a light machine gun, and large numbers were supplied to Britain during the war when it was used to arm Home Guard detachments.

Variants

Ml918 The original model; no bipod, sights not adjustable for windage; selective full automatic or single shot fire.

Ml918Al Hinged butt plate; bipod attached just ahead of the fore-end stock.

Ml922 Basically a 1918 with the barrel finned to improve cooling. Few of this pattern were issued.

Caliber .30in

Length 47. 75in

Weight 22lb

Barrel 24.0in long, 4 grooves, right hand twist

Feed system 20-round detachable box magazine

System of operation Gas; lifting bolt

Rate of fire (cyclic) 5OOrpm

Manufacturers Colt Patent Firearms Manufacturing Co.

Winchester Repeating Arms Co., New Haven, Conn.

Marlin-Rockwell Corporation

*Browning M1917 : 1919*

## Browning M1917 : 1919

The Browning M1917 first entered service with the US Army in 1917. After the war some few changes were made, a new bottom plate, various components of steel instead of bronze, an improved water cooling system and the weapon became the M1917A1.

The mechanism of the Browning relies on the recoil of the barrel; this moves to the rear, carrying the bolt with it. After a short recoil a vertically sliding lock is withdrawn by cam surfaces in the gun body, unlocking the bolt. The final movement of the barrel's recoil causes an accelerator, a curved steel claw, to swing back and, due to leverage gain, flip the bolt backwards very rapidly against a return spring. This movement of the bolt also drives the belt feed mechanism which moves the belt, strips rounds from it and positions them in front of the bolt.

In addition to ground requirements the Browning was wanted as an aircraft gun, but water-cooling was neither necessary nor desirable in this role and an air-cooled model was developed, known as the M1918. From this stemmed the M1919, also air-cooled but with a heavier barrel and intended for use in tanks. During the 1920s it was found that this air-cooled weapon worked well as a ground gun, and eventually the M1914A4 was issued, tripod-mounted, to supplement and later largely replace the water-cooled M1917A1 model.

Calibre .30in
All models 4 grooves, right hand twist
Feed system All models 250-round fabric belt
System of operation All models recoil,vertical sliding breech lock
Rate of fire 450-600rpm
Manufacturers
Remington Arms-UMC
Winchester Arms Co .
Westinghouse Inc.
Colt's Patent Firearms Co.

*CZ 52-57*

## CZ 52-57

The CZ vz52-57 is one of a long line of Czech-produced machine guns that began with the Zbrojovka vz 26 of 1926, a series that gave rise to the Bren gun used in vast numbers by the British army in WW2. Although classed as a light machine gun, this really leans more toward a general-purpose design. The vz52 is little changed from its forebears except in its ability to use magazines or belts without the need for modification. It was originally designed to fire the Czech 7.62 x 45mm cartridge as the vz52, but was then modified to fire the 7.62 x 39mm Soviet round when Warsaw Pact countries standardised on Soviet calibres under the nomenclature CZ vz52/57. The culmination of the series was the CZ vz59, which was a further development of the vz52/57 that dispensed with the magazine feed relying solely on belt fed ammunition.

CARTRIDGE
7.62 x 45mm Czech
7.62 x 39mm Soviet M1941

DIMENSIONS CZ52/57
Length o/a: 1041mm (41.0in) Weight: 7.96kg (17lb 9oz) Barrel: 686mm (27.0in) Rifling: 4grooves rh Feed system: 25-round box or 300 round belt
Rate of fire: 900 rds/min magazine, or1150 rds/min belt

IN PRODUCTION 1952-

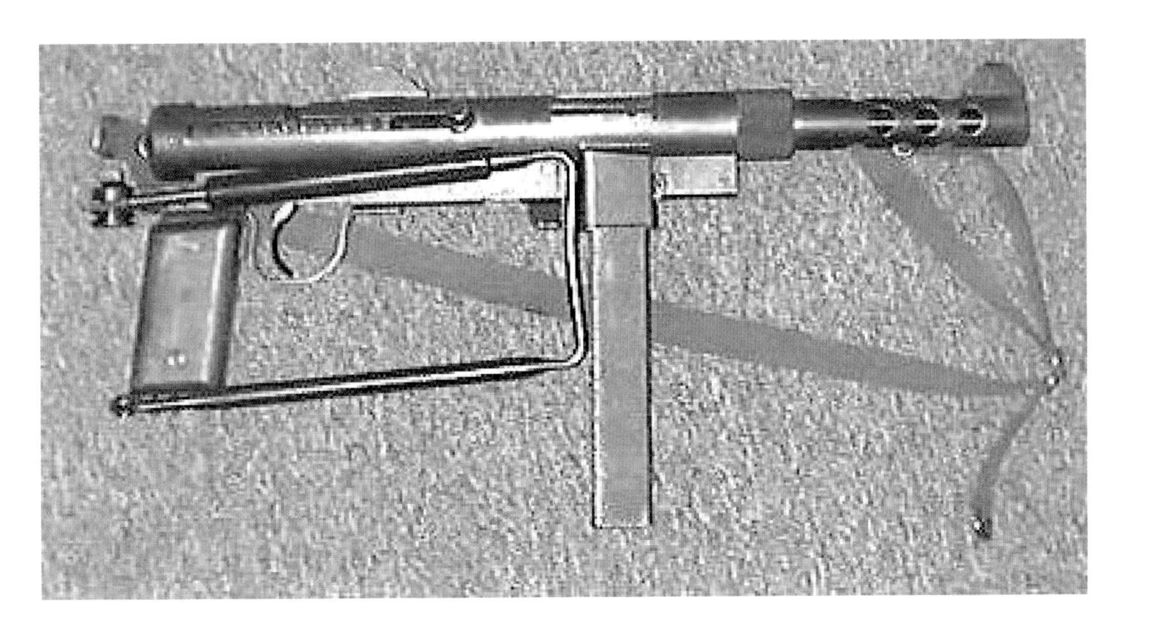

*Carl Gustav 45*

## Carl Gustav 45

One of the oldest submachine guns still in service the Carl Gustav 45 is a robust durable weapon. The original models had no magazine housing and used a drum magazine, but in 1948 a box magazine was developed, and all existing guns were modified to accept the new magazine. The Carl Gustav is used by the Swedish, Irish and Indonesian armies and was also made under licence in Egypt as the 'Port Said'. The US Special Forces in Vietnam used a highly modified version, with an integral silencer replacing the barrel.

CARTRIDGE
9mm Parabellum

DIMENSIONS
Length, stock extended: 808mm (31.8in)
Length, stock folded: 552mm (21.7in)
Barrel: 213mm (8.39in)
Weight empty: 3.90kg (8lb 9oz)
Rifling: 6 grooves, rh
Magazine capacity: 36 rounds Rate of fire: 600rds/min

IN PRODUCTION 1945

*Carl Gustav Anti Tank*

## Carl Gustav Anti Tank

Manufactured by FFV of Sweden, the Carl-Gustaf proved an immediate success and has entered service with the armed forces of many countries. It is a lightweight, portable design; the normal crew is two men, one carrying the launcher, and the other 8 rounds of ammunition.

The Carl-Gustaf is a breech-loaded, percussion-fired weapon. A side primer fires the round and the venturi is opened and closed with a rotary movement. The telescopic sight is mounted on the left hand side and has a x2 magnification and a 17° field of view. Luminous fore and rear sight adapters are available for use during night firing. Designed primarily as an anti-tank weapon, the Carl-Gustaf has been provided with a range of ammunition that has transformed it into an extremely useful infantry support weapon. The following are the rounds available.

Calibre: 84mm
Weight: 29.5kg (packed gun and accessories) 14.2 kg (gun)
.8kg (mount)
1kg (telescopic sight)
Length: 113cm
Range: 400m (HEAT round moving target) 500m (HEAT round stationary target) 1,000m (HE round)
1,000m (smoke round)
2,000m (illuminating round)
Rate of fire: 6 rpm
Crew: 2

*China Type 56*

## China Type 56

The Type 56 is, essentially a Chinese copy of the Kalashnikov, and contrary to the accepted practices of terminology the Type 56 rifle, at 874mm long, is actually shorter than the Type 56 carbine which is 1025mm long; in spite of the fact that carbines are supposed to be shorter than rifles. There are three variants; the Type 56 has a fixed butt and folding bayonet; the 56-1 has a folding stock that passes over the receiver, and the 56-2 has a folding stock which folds sideways to lie along the right side of the receiver. Neither the 56-1 or 56-2 have folding bayonets. All these models are commercially available in semi-automatic form.

CARTRIDGE
7.62 x 39mm Soviet M1941

DIMENSIONS
Length: o/a 874mm (34.40in) Weight: 3.80kg (8lb 6oz) Barrel: 414mm (16.30in) Rifling: 4 grooves, rh Magazine capacity: 30 rounds Rate of fire: 600rds/min

IN PRODUCTION 1958

*China Type 56 carbine*

## CHINA TYPE 56 CARBINE

The Type 56 is a Chinese copy of the Soviet Simonov SKS rifle; any differences between this weapon and the Soviet original are minimal matters of manufacturing convenience. Later versions have a folding spike bayonet in place of the normal folding sword bayonet. It was retired from military service some time ago, except for occasional ceremonial appearances. It is now commercially available as a hunting rifle, albeit without the bayonet.

CARTRIDGE
7.62 x 39mm Soviet M1943

DIMENSIONS
Length o/a: 1025mm (40.35in) Weight: 3.85kg (8lb 8oz) Barrel: 521 mm (2.5in)
Rifling: 4 grooves, rh
Magazine capacity: 10 rounds

IN PRODUCTION 1956-

## China CQ Type automatic rifle

Largely based on the American M16A1, this automatic/semi-automatic weapon is believed to be the first of its kind produced by NORINCO. It is light in weight with a high rate of fire, easy to operate and accurate, with a large capacity magazine. The method of dismantling differs from that of the M16 and it is easily distinguished from the original by the curved shape of its pistol grip.

Calibre: 5.56 mm
Muzzle velocity: 990 m/s
Effective range: 460 metres
Rate of fire:
Automatic: 150-200 rounds/minute
Semi-automatic: 12-15 rounds/minute
Length: 987 mm
Weight unloaded: 3.2 kg
Weight loaded: 3.44 kg
Magazine capacity: 20 rounds
Cartridge data:
Length: 57.4 mm
Weight 11.6 g
Bullet weight: 3.56 g
Average velocity at 25 metres (V25): 965 m/s

## China Red Arrow 8 Anti Tank

weapon to be used against the enemy's tanks and armoured vehicles within an effective range of 100 metres to 3,000 metres. It is a portable weapons system, which can be fired from a kneeling position and if so desired can be mounted on wheeled or tracked vehicles. The missile is tube-launched, optically tracked, with a wire command-link and semi-automatically guided with an infrared system.

Effective range: 100-3,000 metres
Penetration static: >800 mm
Hit probability: > 90%
Flight velocity: 200-240 m/s
Rate of fire: 2-3 rounds/minute
Warhead diameter: 120 mm
Length: 875 mm Weight: 11.2 kg Wing span: 320 mm Weight of launcher (bipod): 47 kg

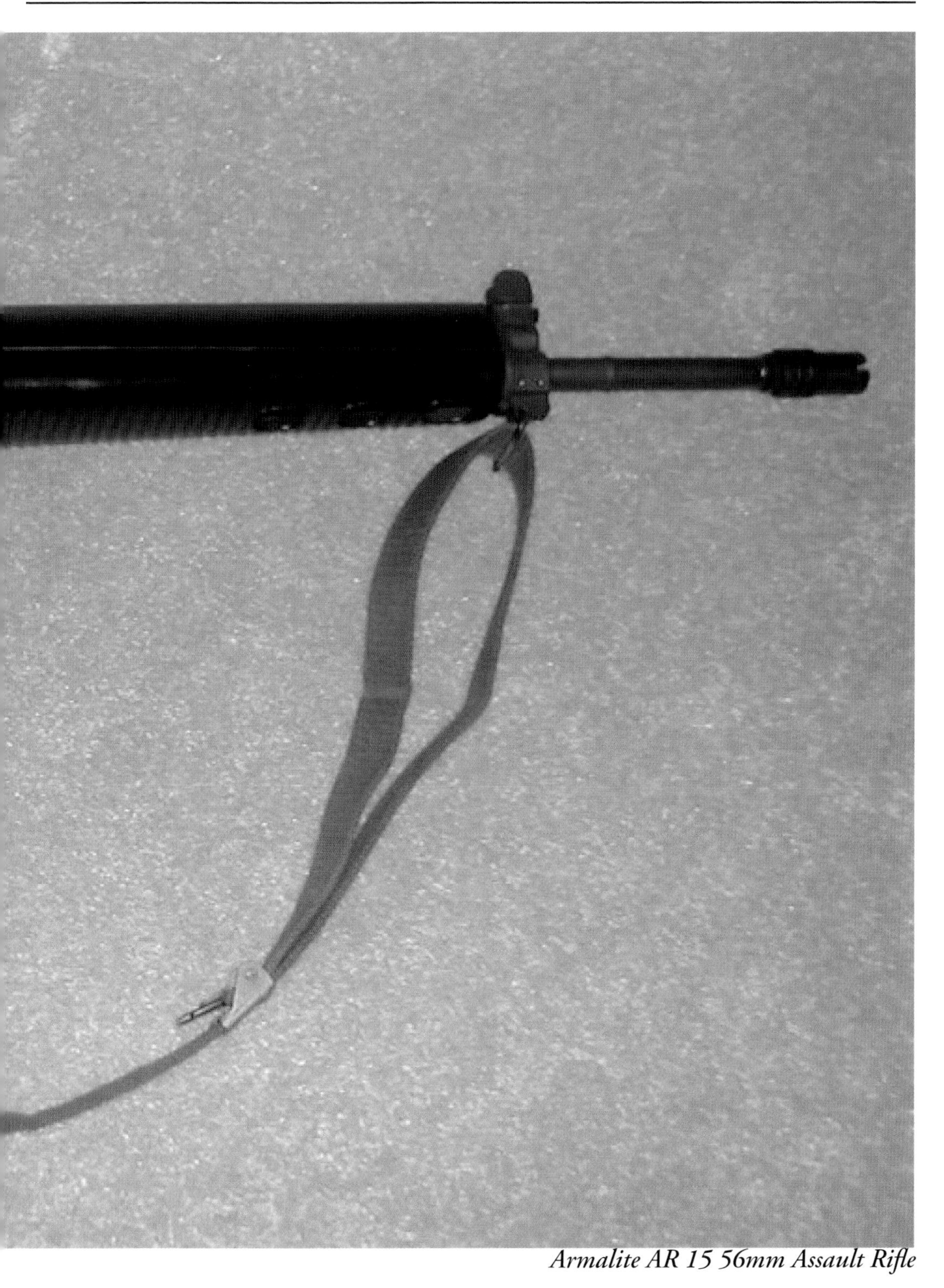

*Armalite AR 15 56mm Assault Rifle*

## China Semi auto sniper rifle

This semi-automatic sniping rifle fires 7.62 mm ball cartridges (with slug) and can be used effectively to a range of 1,000 metres.

Calibre: 7.62 mm
Muzzle velocity: 830 m/s
Effective range: 1,000 metres
Rate of fire: 30 rounds/minute
Overall length: 1,220 mm
Weight with telescope and cheek rest 4.4 kg
Magazine capacity: 10 rounds
Telescopic sight
Magnification: x 4
Field of view: 6°
Exit pupil: 6 mm
Eye relief: 70 mm
Graduated range: 1,000 metres
Graduated direction: 0 - 10 mils
Weight 0.6 kg

## China Type 64 silenced SMG

The Type 64 has an integral silencer and uses a special cartridge based on the 7.63mm Mauser but with a pointed, heavy bullet fired at subsonic velocity. The mechanism combines the blow back action and bolt of the Soviet PPS-43 submachine gun with the trigger mechanism of the Czech ZB26 machine gun. The silencer is a Maxim type, full of baffles and with a perforated barrel. With the special cartridges it is reasonably silent, but with standard full-charge pistol ammunition it produces almost as much noise as a conventional, un-silenced weapon.

CARTRIDGE
7.62 x 25mm Type P Subsonic

DIMENSIONS
Length, stock extended; 843mm (33.3in)
Length, stock retracted: 635mm (25.0in)
Barrel: 244mm (9.6in) Weight, empty: 3.40kg (71b 8oz)
Rifling: 4 grooves, rh
Magazine capacity: 30 rounds Rate of fire: 1300 rds/min

IN PRODUCTION 1966

## China Type 74 light MG

This light machine-gun is a principal infantry weapon and fires 7.62 mm Type 56 cartridges. This LMG is of simple construction, easy operation and is drum-fed, although the magazine for the 7.62 mm sub-machine-gun Type 56 can also be used. It is fitted with a bipod, a wooden butt and pistol grip.

Calibre: 7.62 mm
Muzzle velocity: 735 m/s Effective range: 600 metres Rate of fire: 150 rounds/minute Length: 1,070 mm
Weight (drum empty): 6.2 kg Drum capacity: 101 rounds

## China Type 79 sub MG

This extremely lightweight sub-machine-gun is designed primarily for airborne and subversive units. It fires 7.62 mm calibre, Type 51 pistol cartridges (the Chinese made 7.62 x 25mm Soviet Pistol), and has an effective range up to 200 metres. It is of lightweight, simple construction; and this combined with its small size makes it an easy weapon to carry. The Type 79 is capable of single shot or automatic fire. The Type 79 is a gas operated weapon, using a short-stroke tappet above the barrel that forces back an operating rod to drive a rotating bolt; the system is similar to that employed in the AK series of rifles, as are the outer controls such as the safety and pistol grip, making it easier to train soldiers already familiar with the rifle. It is remarkably light for a submachine gun, due to the rotating bolt system which removes the requirement for the heavy bolt necessary in a simple blow back weapon.

CARTRIDGE
7.62 x 25mm Soviet Pistol

DIMENSIONS
Length, stock extended: 740mm (29.13in)
Length, stock retracted: 470mm (18.5in)
Barrel: 225mm (8.86in) Weight, empty: 1.90kg (41b 8oz)
Rifling: -
Magazine capacity: 20 rounds Rate of fire: 650 rds/min

IN PRODUCTION 1980

## China Type 80 Multi-purpose MG

An effective infantry weapon, this machine gun fires 7.62 mm, Type 53 cartridges, with an effective range of 1,000 metres. It is of lightweight, simple construction, and manufactured to a high standard of precision. The Type 80 is a multi-purpose weapon, adaptable for both anti-aircraft and flat trajectory fire. It is equally capable of fulfilling the offensive light machine-gun, and the defensive heavy machine-gun roles. Incorporated with a muzzle compensator which helps to stabilize the gun when firing, is a flash hider to reduce the chance of the firing position being spotted. All vulnerable parts of the mechanism are protected with dust covers at. The rear sight is arched, making it easy to adjust for short range fire.

Calibre: 7.62 mm
Muzzle velocity: 825 m/s
Effective range: 1, 000 metres
Rate of fire: 350 rounds/minute
Length: 1,192 mm
Barrel length: 675 mm
Total weight (including bipod): 12.6 kg Fire area at flat trajectory fire:
Traverse: 73°
Elevation: -13°- + 18°
Fire area at anti-aircraft fire:
Maximum elevation: 72°
Magazine box capacity: 100 or 200 rounds

## China Type 81 Automatic Rifle

An effective infantry weapon, this machine gun fires 7.62 mm, Type 53 cartridges, with an effective range of 1,000 metres. It is of lightweight, simple construction, and manufactured to a high standard of precision. The Type 80 is a multi-purpose weapon, adaptable for both anti-aircraft and flat trajectory fire. It is equally capable of fulfilling the offensive light machine-gun, and the defensive heavy machine-gun roles. Incorporated with a muzzle compensator which helps to stabilize the gun when firing, is a flash hider to reduce the chance of the firing position being spotted. All vulnerable parts of the mechanism are protected with dust covers at. The rear sight is arched, making it easy to adjust for short range fire.

Calibre: 7.62 mm
Muzzle velocity:
Rifle: 720 m/s
LMG: 735 m/s
Effective range:
Rifle: 400 metres
LMG: 600 metres
Rate of firing combat condition at semi-automatic: 45 rounds/minute
Full automatic: 100-115 rounds/minute
Overall length:
Rifle fixed stock: 955 mm
Folding stock: 730 mm
With bayonet 1,105 mm
LMG: 1,024 mm
Total weight
Rifle, fixed stock (magazine empty): 3.4 kg
Rifle, folding stock (magazine empty): 3.5 kg
LMG (magazine empty): 5.3 kg
Magazine capacity:
Rifle: 30 rounds (interchangeable with LMG)
LMG: 75 rounds (interchangeable with rifle)

*Colt SMG & HK-MP5*

## Colt SMG

This is a 9mm submachine gun based on the well-known M16 rifle configuration, so that the training time is reduced when soldiers already familiar with the rifle are given this weapon. The butt-stock is telescopic, and the only outward difference between this and the various short M16 type rifles is the long, thin magazine. Purchasers had the option of full automatic fire or three-round bursts mechanism, and the fire selector switch marking will indicate which has been fitted. It is also possible to have a purely semi-automatic model with no automatic or burst-fire capability.

CARTRIDGE
9mm Parabellum

DIMENSIONS
Length, stock extended: 730mm (28.75in)
Length, stock retracted: 650mm (25.6in)
Barrel: 260mm (10.25in) Weight, empty: 2.59kg (51b 11oz)
Rifling: 6 grooves rh
Magazine capacity: 20 or 32 rounds Rate of fire: 900 rds/min

IN PRODUCTION 1990

*Sub-mach gun, ZK383*

## Sub-mach gun, ZK383

The ZK383 was developed in Czechoslovakia in the early 1930s and went into production in 1933. Early models are reported to have had a front pistol grip but this was soon abandoned for the wooden fore-end pattern. It is unusual in that it was provided with a bipod for steadying it when fired in the prone position, and was apparently conceived as a sort of squad light machine gun rather than the usual hip-fired role of the sub-machine gun. Another unusual feature for this class of weapon was the provision for quick-changing the barrel. Another pointer to the squad automatic role.

The mechanism is a simple blowback with the return spring housed in a tube in the butt, the bolt having a connecting link pinned to its rear end to press against the cap on the return spring. As it stands the bolt weighs 1lb 9oz and the gun fires at 500rpm, but a removable section of the bolt, weighing six ounces, can be taken out to lighten the bolt and thus increase the rate of fire to 700rpm.

The ZK383 was widely sold abroad in the years before the war and was adopted by the Bulgarian Army. When the Germans occupied Czechoslovakia, the CZ factory was taken over and re-organized as the Waffenwerke Brunn AG. Production of the ZK383 was continued, the entire output being taken by the SS and used in battle on the Russian Front. The weapon continued in production after the war, the factory having reverted to its original ownership and name, production finally ending in late 1948.

Calibre 9mm
Length 35.5in
Weight 10lb 8oz
Barrel 12.75in long, 6 grooves, right hand twist
Feed system 30-round detachable box magazine
System of operation Blow back, selective
Rate of fire (cyclic 500 or 700rpm
Manufacturer Czeskoslovenska Zbroyowka Brno

*DShK 1938*

## DShK 1938

Degtyarev first developed a heavy machine gun, the DK, in 1934 but it was only made in prototype form and underwent further development before being adopted in 1938 as the DShK. The initials indicate the appearance of a second designer, Georg S. Shpagin, later a Lieutenant-general of the Red Army and designer of the PPSh sub- machine gun. Degtyarev laid out the general design and basic mechanism, while Shpagin was responsible for the feed mechanism. Special attention to the feed was demanded by the fact that the weapon was designed to use the large 12.7mm cartridge, and the weight of a full belt of this placed a considerable strain on the feed system. Shpagin's solution was to mount a rotary 'squirrel-cage' rotating block above the bolt. The long barrel was heavily finned to aid cooling and a single baffle muzzle brake used to try and reduce the recoil force. The mounting was a tripod which, for transport, folded and was fitted with a pair of wheels so that it resembled the Maxim's 'Sokolov' mounting. This tripod could be erected some five feet high so that the weapon could be used as an anti-aircraft machine gun, a role in which it was very prominent during World War II.

At the end of the war it was modified by removing the rotating drum feed and replacing it with a simple swinging-arm pattern which had been developed for a postwar gun, and as the DShKM it remains in service today. Numbers of DShK were supplied to various satellite countries, and it was particularly prominent as an anti-aircraft weapon during the Korean War.

Calibre 12.7mm
Length 62.5in
Weight 78lb 8oz
Barrel 42.0in long, 4 grooves, right hand twist
Feed system 50-round belt
System of operation
Gas; hinged locking struts
Rate of fire 550rpm
Manufacturer State Arsenals

*Daewoo K2*

## Daewoo K2

A gas operated, selective fire rifle with a folding plastic butt, the weapon can fire single shots, three round bursts or fully automatic. This is controlled by the three-position, combined safety and fire selector switch on left side of receiver. When turned so that the pointer is forward the weapon is safe, turned to the vertical it will produce single shots, and to the rear automatic fire or three-round bursts. The barrel is fitted with a muzzle brake and compensator that also doubles as a grenade-launcher. The three round burst mechanism is unusual in that it does not re-set to zero if a part burst is fired; so that if only two shots of a burst are fired, the next pull of the trigger will fire a single shot.

CARTRIDGE 5.56mm x 45

DIMENSIONS
Length, butt extended: 38.98in (990mm);
Length, butt folded: 28.74in (730mm)
Weight unloaded: 7lb 3oz (3.26kg)
Barrel: 18.30in (465mm)
Rifling: 6 grooves, rhMagazine: capacity 30-rounds Rate of fire: 650 rds/min
IN PRODUCTION: 1987-

*DeLisle silent carbine*

## DeLisle silent carbine

When the Second World War started there were very few silent firearms in the world. In 1942 William De Lisle and Sir Malcolm Campbell (of combined operations HQ) began work on a totally silent rifle for use on covert operations. The De Lisle carbine was proposed to the Ordnance Board in 1943 by De Lisle. The design as accepted made use of the American .45 Automatic Colt Pistol (ACP) round because it travelled at subsonic velocities and therefore did not make a distinctive crack as it reached the speed of sound. This particular round was chosen because it was already in British service for the Thompson sub machine gun and the Colt Model 1911 pistol, the magazine for which could be modified and used in the De Lisle rifle. Despite the fact that the .45 ACP round was only a pistol cartridge the De Lisle had a barrel length of 8.27 inches, compared with the 5 inches of the Colt 1911. This noticeably increased range and accuracy.

Used or condemned SMLE rifles were used as the basis for the De Lisle. The receiver had the charger guide removed and an ejector set into the left of the body. The magazine housing was modified to take Colt 1911 magazines and it was re-chambered for .45 ACP ammunition. The bolt was shortened to 3.6inches and the bolt head recessed and extractor modified.

Cartridge: .45 ACP
Length o/a: 960mm (37.80in)
Weight: 3.70kg (8lb 2oz)
Barrel Length: 210mm (8.27in)
Rifleing: 4 grooves lh
Feed: 8 round removable box magazine
In production: 1942-1945
Markings:Maker, date and SHT LE on right side of stock band
Safety:Manual safety catch on left of action. Press forward to fire and rearward for safe
Unloading: Press up magazine catch inside trigger guard to release magazine which should be removed and emptied. Open bolt and inspect chamber for any rounds. Close bolt, fire off action and replace magazine

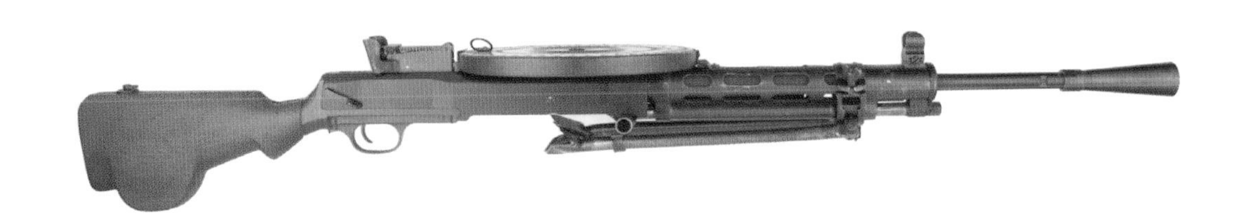

*Degtyarev DP 1928*

## Degtyarev DP 1928

The DP28 was designed in 1921 by Vasili Alekseivitch Dagtyarev and, adopted by the Soviet Army in 1928 as their standard light machine gun under the designation Ruchnoi Pulyemet Degtyaryeva Pekhotnii (Automatic weapon, Degtyarev, infantry) or DP.

The gun was of simple but reasonably robust construction and contained a mere 65 parts, only six of them moving. The weapon had some deficiencies, most especially excessive friction in the action, susceptibility to the ingress of dirt, and overheating because barrel removal was difficult. The first guns had finned barrels to help dissipate the heat, but the problem was never fully overcome and the rate of fire had to be limited to the capacity of the barrel to disperse heat. Also the drum magazine was made of sheet steel and was liable to distort if dropped or roughly handled.

The gun was gas-operated, and the feed arrangement was reasonably good, rimmed cartridges usually cause problems in light automatic weapons, but are generally worse in those using box magazines. The large flat single deck drum of the Degtyarev, driven by a clockwork mechanism rather than by the action of the gun, at least eliminates the problem of double feed. The magazine was originally 49 rounds, generally reduced in practice to 47 rounds to reduce the chance of jams

The DP was a very good design, particularly well suited to the Soviet Army. It was uncomplicated, and did not demand highly skilled labour or complex machinery to produce.It was simple to operate and was, like most Russian equipment extremely robust.

Calibre 7.62mm
length 50.8in
Weight 20Ib 8oz
Barrel 23.8in long, 4 grooves, right hand twist
Feed system 47-round detachable drum
System of operation Gas; locking struts
Rate of fire (cyclic) 550rpm
Manufacturer Tula Arsenal

*Dragunov*

## Dragunov

Entering service in 1971, Dragon, a lightweight, portable missile was designed as a medium-range weapon to provide infantry platoons with a reasonable anti-armour capability.

Each missile is supplied sealed in a glass-fibre launch tube with the launch charge contained in a bulky circular container at the rear end. The operator attaches this to his tracker unit, which comprises of a telescopic sight, IR sensor and electronics box. When the missile is fired three curved fins flick open to provide spin stabilisation. The operator holds the sight on the target and the tracker automatically controls the missile onto the line of sight by firing appropriate pairs of side thrusters. After use the launch tube is thrown away and a fresh one attached to the tracker.

Although the Dragon system proved effective in operations during Operation Just Cause in Grenada, and during the First Gulf War, it is not without its problems. Perhaps the most important is that the missile body diameter of 4.5in (11.4cm) sets the limit on the size of the warhead. The effectiveness of a shaped charge warhead is a function of its diameter, and at least 6in (15cm) is likely to be needed to counter the new armours coming into service on the latest Soviet tanks. In addition, the missile is slow; the operator, must hold his breath throughout the flight of the missile, and any movement of the operator's shoulder at the moment of launch, can send the missile into the ground. There is also a tendency for the rocket thrusters to deteriorate in storage, and many need early replacement.

Type: Infantry anti-tank/assault missile.
Dimensions:
Length 29.3in (74cm); body diameter 4.5in (11.4cm); fin span 13in (33cm).
Launch weight: 24,41b (11.1 kg).
Propulsion: Initially by a recoilless gas-generator thruster in the launch tube; sustained propulsion is provided by 60 small side thrusters fired in pairs upon tracker demand. Guidance: See text.
Range: 200 to 3,300ft (60-1,000m).
Flight speed: About 230mph (370km/h).
Warhead: Linear shaped charge, 5.41b (2.45kg).

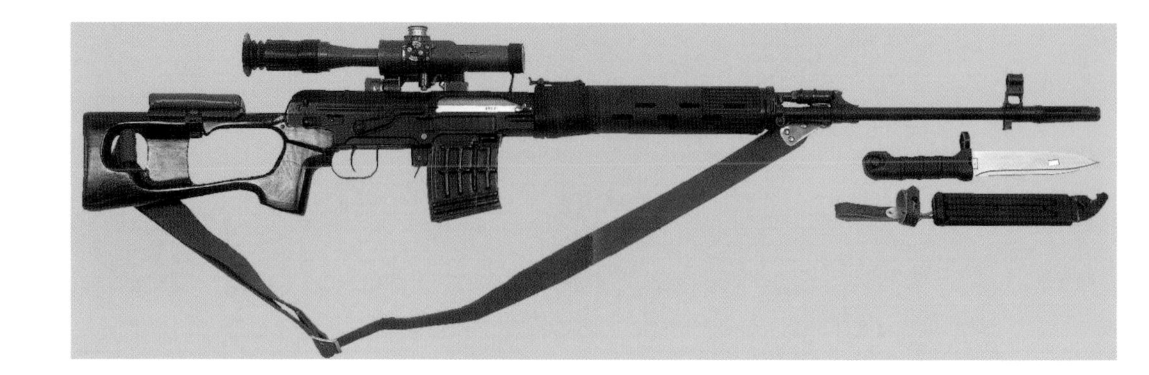

*Dragunov SVD*

## Dragunov SVD

Although similar to the Kalashnikov in principle, the Dragunov rifle differs in using a short stroke piston to operate the bolt carrier; the AK series uses a long-stroke piston, which would be inappropriate in this case, since this is a sniping rifle and the shift of balance during a long-stroke piston's movement can degrade the accuracy. The rifle is normally provided with the PSO-1 telescope sight. This is secured to the left side of the receiver and has a magnification of x 4. The PSO-1 is unusual in that it incorporates an infra-red detector to enable its use as a passive night sight, though the image intensifying night sight NSPU-3 is also an item of issue with this rifle. The Dragunov saw service not only in the former USSR but also the Warsaw Pact nations, as well as several Soviet client states. It saw widespread action in Afghanistan where some examples ended up in the hands of the Mujahideen. It is claimed to have an effective range of 1000.

CARTRIDGE 762 x 54R Soviet

DIMENSIONS
Length o/a:1225mm (4822in) Weight: 431 kg (91b 8oz) Barrel: 610mm (240in)
Rifling: 4 grooves, rh Magazine capacity: 10 rounds

IN PRODUCTION 1963-.

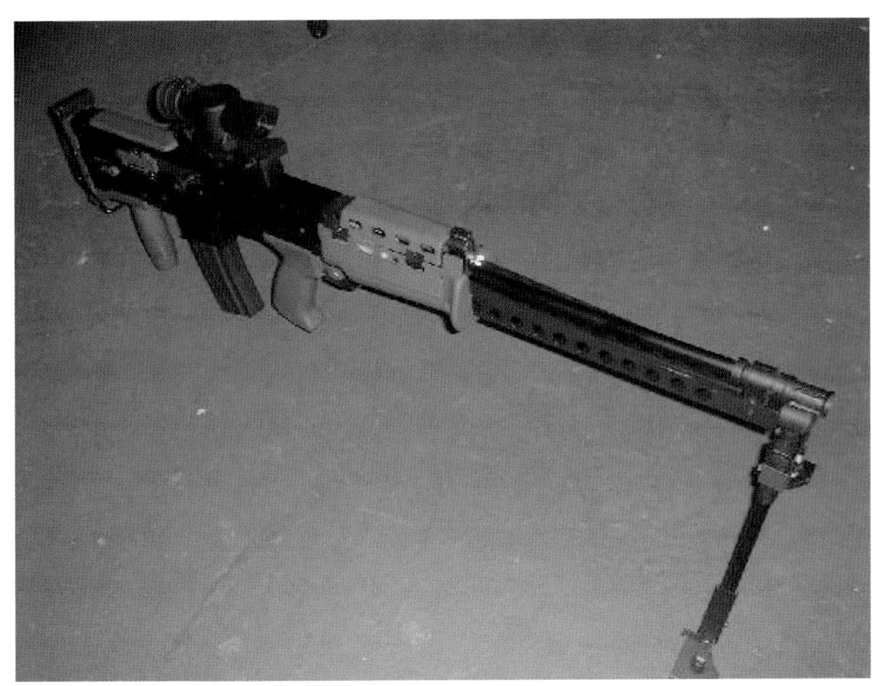

*Enfield L86 LSW*

## Enfield L86 LSW

The Enfield L86 is one half of the Enfield Weapon System that, together with the L85A1 standard assault rifle equips the modern British infantry. It is the current British 5.56mm Light Support Weapon or squad automatic weapon, and shares around 80 percent of its components with the L85 rifle. It is a bullpup design, and has a heavier and longer barrel than the L85, the mechanism has been altered so that when set to automatic it stops firing with the breech held open, while when set for single shots it stops with the breech closed and a fresh round loaded. At single shot it is exceptionally accurate, a function of the longer and heavier barrel.

CARTRIDGE 5.56 x 45mm NATO

DIMENSIONS
Length o/a: 900mm (35.43in) Weight: 540kg (11lb 14oz) Barrel: 646mm (25.4in) Rifling: 6 grooves, rh
Feed system: 30-round box magazine
Rate of fire: 700 rds/min

IN PRODUCTION 1985-

*FA MAS*

## FA MAS

The FA MAS, or Fusil d'Assaut de la Manufacture d'Armes St Etienne, is the current standard French Army rifle and was the first 'bullpup' design to enter military service. It uses a two-part bolt in a delayed blow back system and has the chamber fluted to avoid difficult extraction, so that Cartridges fired from this weapon are easily recognised by their longitudinal marks. It handles well and shoots accurately, and can also launch grenades. A rotary switch inside the front of the trigger guard acts as a combined safety-catch and fire-selector.There is also a training version that has been adapted to fire inert pellets, propelled using a sparklet gas bottle. This version is in all other respects exactly like the service weapon.

In 1994 a new model, the F2, appeared with a full-sized hand-guard instead of a small trigger guard and a NATO-standard magazine housing to accept M16 type magazines. All 5.56mm ammunition will chamber in this weapon but optimum performance is only achieved with the French service ammunition. The bipod has been replaced with a sling swivel and the grenade launcher removed, although a bipod and grenade-launcher are issued separately.

CARTIDGE 5.56 x 45mmType France

DIMENSIONS
Length o/a: 757mm (29.80in) Weight:3.61kg (7lb 5oz)Barrel: 488mm (19.2in) Rifling: 6 grooves, rh Magazine capacity: 25 rounds Rate of fire: 950 rds/min

IN PRODUCTION 1975

SAFETY
When parallel with the bore it is set safe; when switched to the right it gives single shots, and when to the left, automatic fire. With the switch in the automatic position, operation of a burst-limiting button, beneath the butt stock and behind the magazine, brings in a three-round burst limiter.

*FH Minimi*

## FH Minimi

With the adoption of the 5.56mm round as the standard NATO rifle round, there emerged a need for a light machine in the smaller calibre. The new weapon is a squad support weapon only, since the 5.56mm round is simply not powerful enough to be used in the heavy machine gun role, The FN Minimi was designed to extract the utmost performance from the 5.56mm cartridge and has acquired a reputation for reliability. It is gas operated, using a simple rotating bolt system, and although normally belt fed it can accept M16-type magazines without any modification having to be made. A special cover plate closes the belt aperture when a magazine is loaded, or closes the magazine aperture when a belt is in place, so that there is no danger of trying to double-feed. There is a light, short-barrelled paratroop version with a collapsible butt, and a slightly modified version of the standard model is produced for the US Army as the M249 machine gun.

CARTRIDGE 5.56 x 45mm NATO

DIMENSIONS
Length o/a: 1040mm (41.0in) Weight: 685kg (15lb 2oz) Barrel: 466mm (18.35in) Rifling: 6 grooves, rh
Feed system: 30-round box magazine, or 200 round belt
Rate of fire: 700-1000 rds/min

IN PRODUCTION 1982-

*FN F2000 56mm NATO Assault Rifle*

## FARA 83

The FARA 83 was developed in the early 1980s for the Argentine Army. It was designed locally and uses a conventional gas piston, bolt carrier and rotating bolt method of operation. Financial problems led to slow production and for some time only part of the army were re-equipped with this weapon.

There is a manual safety catch inside the trigger guard and a fire selector for either single shots or automatic fire.

The cocking handle lies on top of the gas cylinder, well forward of the receiver and actually operates on the gas piston, which has the bolt carrier machined as an integral part. One variant was produced with a bipod attached below the gas block, and a special fore-end with a recess to accept the folded bipod legs. The pitch of the rifling is such that either M193 or NATO ammunition can be used.

CARTRIDGE 5.56 x 45mm

DIMENSIONS
Length, stock extended: 1000mm (39.37in)
Length, stock folded: 745mm (29.33in)
Weight: 3.95kg (8lb 11oz) Barrel: 452mm (17.8in) Rifling: 6 grooves, rh Magazine capacity: 30 rounds Rate of fire: 750 rds/min

IN PRODUCTION 1984-90

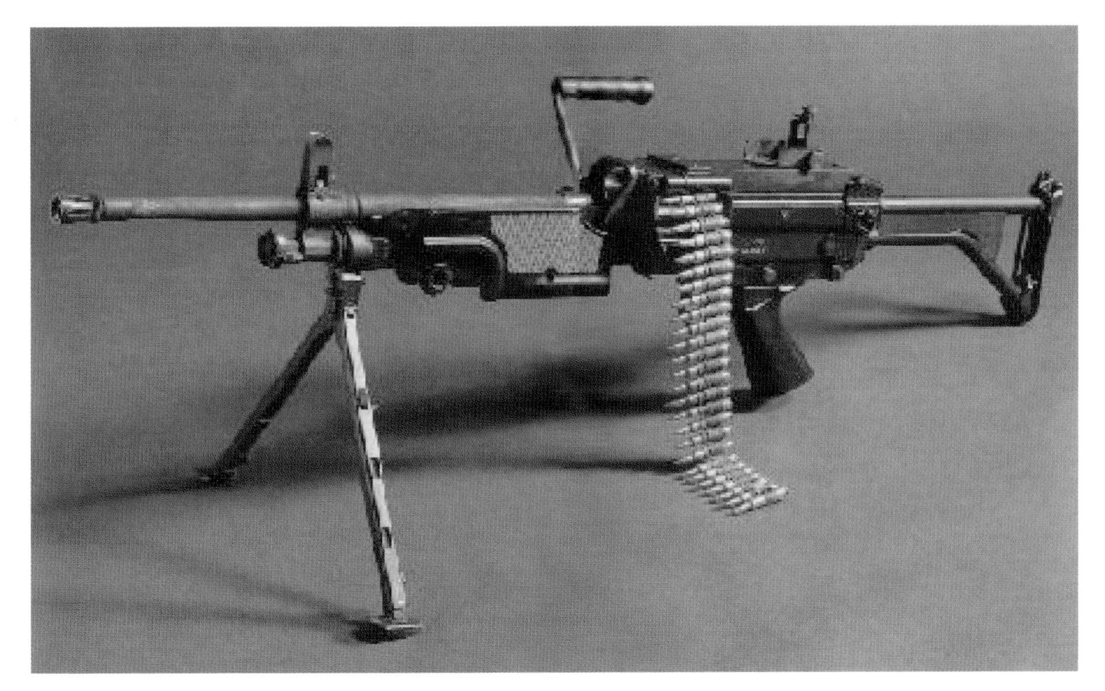

*FN M429*

## FN 1949

Development of the FN 1949 started in the 1930s but progress was halted for the duration of the war, and it was not until 1949 that work was completed. It was adopted in various calibres by Egypt, Argentina, Luxembourg, Brazil and Colombia and was reliable, if rather expensive. The locking system used a gas-operated, tilting bolt, and there is a manual safety catch on the right side of the trigger guard. The magazine was loaded using a charger, through the top of the open action. The FN 1949's main claim to fame however is that it was the forerunner of the later, and better-known, FAL model.

CARTRIDGE 7.92 x 57mm

DIMENSIONS
Length o/a: 1116mm (43.54in)
Weight: 4.31kg (9lb 8oz) Barrel: 590mm (23.23in) Rifling: 4 grooves, rh Magazine capacity: 10 rounds Rate of fire: single shot only

IN PRODUCTION 1950-58

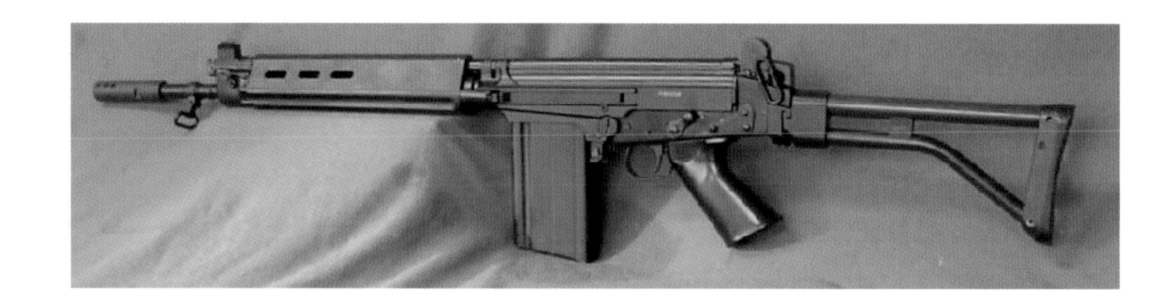



## FN FAL

Developed by Fabrique Nationale of Belgium from the earlier FN 1949, the FN-FAL, or Fusil Automatique Legere, is probably the most widely used rifle in history. It has been adopted by over 90 countries, many of whom have demanded their own minor modifications. Several countries have manufactured their own weapons under license and, again, have incorporated their own modifications. In the UK after lengthy trials and various modifications it was produced for the British forces as the L1A1. The L1A1 was also produced under license in India and Australia.

The FN factory produced four standard models; the fixed-butt rifle 50-00; the folding butt rifle 50-64; a folding-butt carbine 50-63; and a fixed-butt heavy-barrel model with bipod 50-41. Most models were available in either semi-automatic only or selective-fire form.

CARTRIDGE 7.62 x 51mm NATO

DIMENSIONS
Length o/a: 1090mm (42.9in) Weight: 445kg (9lb 13oz) Barrel: 533mm (21.0in)
Rifling: 4 grooves, rh Magazine capacity: 20 rounds Rate of fire: 650 rds/min

IN PRODUCTION 1953-

*FN FNC*

## FN FNC

The FN FNC is effectively a development of the CAL, an abortive attempt to produce a successor to the ubiquitous FN FAL. It introduced at a time when the potential customers were aware of the NATO adoption of a 5.56mm cartridge, it was also cheaper and more reliable than the CAL and consequently it met with a better reception. Steel, alloy and plastic have been used in the construction, and steel pressings have been employed where ever possible to ease production. The mechanism is similar to that of the CAL, gas operated with a rotating bolt, and the magazine interface is NATO standard and will accept M16 and similar types of magazine. There is a combined safety catch and fire selector lever is on the left side of the receiver above the trigger. In Indonesia it was produced as the Pindad SS1, and in Sweden as the Bofors AK-5.

CARTRIDGE 5.56 x 45mm NATO

DIMENSIONS
Length, stock extended: 997mm (39.25in)
Length, stock folded: 766mm (30.16in)
Weight: 3.80kg (8lb 6oz) Barrel: 450mm (17.71 in) Rifling: 6 grooves, rh Magazine capacity: 30 rounds Rate of fire: 700 rds/min

IN PRODUCTION 1979-

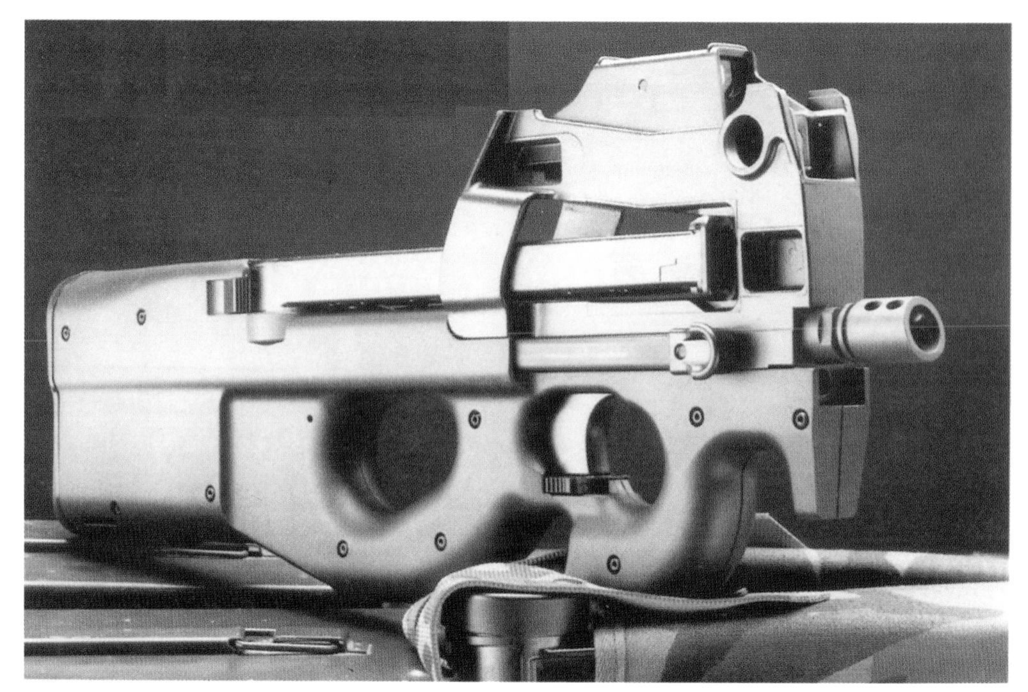

*FN Herstal P90*

## FN Herstal P90

Production of the P-90, otherwise known as the PDW or Personal Defence Weapon began in the early 1990s, and the entire output is destined for military use. Despite its unusual appearance and synthetic casing the P90 relies on conventional internal blow back operation. The magazine is transparent and is unique in lying above the weapon with the cartridges at 90 degrees to the barrel axis. The rounds are fed via a turntable mechanism and empty cases are ejected downward through the hollow pistol grip. The penetrative power of the bullet is said to be formidable.

CARTRIDGE
5.7 x 28mm

DIMENSIONS
Length o/a: 500mm (19.68in)
Barrel: 263mm (10.35in) Weight, empty: 2.54kg (5lb 9oz)
Rifling: 6 grooves rh
Magazine capacity: 50 rounds Rate of fire: 900 rds/min

IN PRODUCTION 1990

*Finland Suomi, Model 1931*

## FINLAND SUOMI, MODEL 1931

This weapon was one of the designs of the Finnish firearms expert A. J. Lahti. He produced his first sub-machine gun in the early 1920s and gradually improved and refined the design until this model, which was issued to the Finnish Army in 1931; it was not patented until 1932 and is sometimes referred to as the Model of 1932.

The Suomi was exceptionally well made, and was extremely reliable and accurate. It was unusual in being provided with a means of quickly changing the barrel. As well as being made in Finland, it was also manufactured under license in Sweden, Denmark and Switzerland, and adopted by the armies of those countries. It was widely sold throughout the world and was used in large numbers in the Spanish Civil War .

The operation of the Suomi is by the usual blow back system, firing from an open bolt. The cocking handle is rather oddly positioned beneath the rear cap of the receiver and is so designed that it remains still while the gun is firing. Of the various magazines provided for the weapon, the 71-round drum was adopted by the Soviets as their standard pattern after they had first-hand experience of the effectiveness of the Suomi in the Winter War of 1940-41. After this affair the Suomi turned up in the hands of Soviet troops in the Leningrad area when the German Army besieged the city. It was also used by elements of the Norwegian Army in their brief campaign against the Germans in 1940.

Calibre 9mm
Length 34.25in
Weight 10lb 5oz
Barrel 12.5in long, 6 grooves, right hand twist
Feed system 20- or 50-round box, 40- or 71-round drum
System of operation Blow back, selective fire
Rate of fire (cyclic) 900rpm
Menufacturer Oy Tikkakoski AB, Sakara, Rnland

## GAU 19A

Developed by General Electric, the GAU 19A is a three-barrelled Gatling-type weapon requiring an external source of power such as a vehicle battery. Although it produces a much higher volume of fire than a standard M2HB gun, it is only slightly heavier and transmits less recoil force to its mounting. It can be adjusted to give two rates of fire, either 1000 or 2000 rounds per minute as required. The mechanism is based upon the Gatling gun system with the three barrels rotating in front of a receiver unit in which cam tracks control the movement of the three bolts. The gun will fire any type of 50 Browning ammunition, including SLAP discarding sabot rounds. A de-linking feed system accepts standard machine gun belts and removes the rounds from the belt prior to feeding into the linkless supply chutes. Safety in this weapon is controlled by simply cutting off the power supply to the breech rotor, and is a function on the control box rather than a mechanism on the gun.

CARTRIDGE .50 Browning

DIMENSIONS
Length: o/a 1181mm (4650in) Weight: unloaded 33.60kg 74lb 1oz
Barrel: 914mm (36.0in)
Rifling 11 grooves, rh
Feed system: linkless feed
Cyclic rate: Selectable 1000 or 2000 rds/min

IN PRODUCTION 1986-

## GIAT FR1, FR2

The GIAT FR1 and FR2 sniping rifles are both employed by the French army and, like their British counterpart the L42, were modified from an existing service rifle, in this case the pre-war MAS36. That however is where the similarity ends, for although the GIAT is based on the action of the MAS 36 it has been heavily modified for its new role as a precision sniping rifle; it was actually designed in the first instance as a target rifle, and only later modified for the sniping role. The Fl was issued first in 7.5mm calibre, and then changed to 7.62mm calibre in the late 1970s. The FR2 model, introduced in 1984 is an improved version; the fore-end is made of plastic-covered metal instead of wood, the bipod is stronger, and there is a thermal insulating sleeve over the barrel to prevent warping due to heat and to reduce the infra-red signature.

CARTRIDGE
7.5 x 54mm or 7.62 x 51mm

DIMENSIONS
Length o/a: 1138mm (44.8in) Weight: 520kg (11lb 7oz) Barrel- 552mm (22.9in)
Rifling- 4 grooves rh Magazine capacity- 10 rounds

IN PRODUCTION
1966-80 (F1); 1984- (F2)

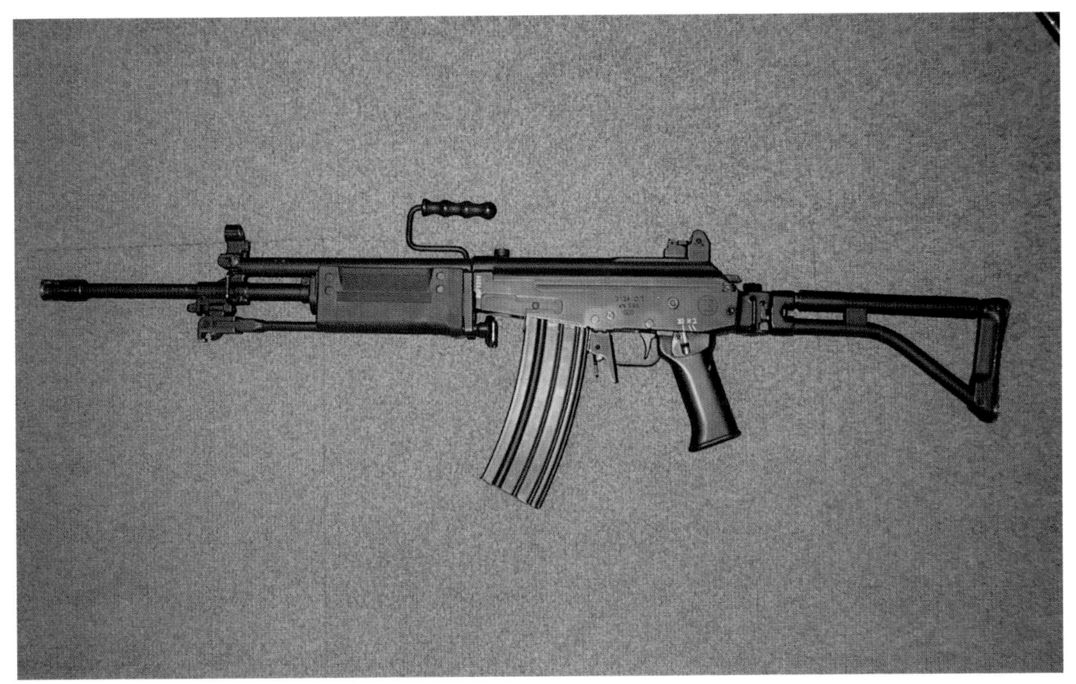

*Galil*

## Galil

The Galil is an indigenous design, based on a modified version of the Kalashnikov rotating bolt system. It does bear a strong resemblance to the Valmet assault rifles indeed, the first rifles were built using Valmet tooling, at least for the bodies. It was originally developed in 5.56mm calibre, but later a 7.62 x 51mm model was also produced, though this was never as popular as the 5.56mm version. It is of course, used by the Israeli Defence Forces and has also been adopted by several Central American and African armies.

There are three main versions of the Galil. The Galil ARM has a bipod and carrying handle, the Galil AR with no bipod and carrying handle, and the Galil SAR. This is the short barrel version of the AR. All three have folding stocks and are fitted with bottle openers to prevent soldiers using other parts of the gun to open bottles.

The Galil is produced under license in South Africa as the R4.

CARTRIDGE 5.56 x 45mm M193

DIMENSIONS
Length, stock extended: 979mm (38.54in)
Length, stock folded: 742mm (29.2in)
Weight: 3.95kg (8lb 11oz) Barrel: 460mm (18.1in)
Rifling: 6 grooves, rh Magazine capacity: 35 or 50 rounds
Rate of fire- 550 rds/min

IN PRODUCTION 1971-

*Gewehr 43*

## Gewehr 43

Experience with the Gewehr 41(W) soon showed the areas in which improvement was desirable. The lessons learnt from the earlier weapon were incorporated in the design of its successor the Gewehr 43. The whole weapon was much lighter and better balanced than its predecessor, and, moreover, had been designed with rapid production in mind so that it was an easier proposition to turn out in quantity. One unusual feature (for a military rifle) was the inclusion in the design of a machined-out dovetail section on the receiver to act as a seating for a sighting telescope, and a large number of these rifles were issued for sniping, fitted with the Zundblickfernrohr 4 telescope.

The G43 was extensively used on the Eastern Front, being first issued in 1943 and was much less common on other fronts. As a result of the increasing difficulty of production in Germanythere was a gradual change in the appearance of the weapon as produced in 1944 and 1945; originally finished to a reasonably high standard and with solid wooden furniture, the external finish gradually deteriorated until final versions exhibited numerous tool-marks, and the furniture was of resin-bonded plywood laminations or phenolic plastic compounds. Nevertheless, the internal quality was always to a satisfactory standard, and the weapon had a good reputation for accuracy and reliability. It remained in production until the end of the war and was afterwards adopted by the Czech Army as their standard sniping rifle.

Caliber 7.92mm
Length 44.0in
Weight 91b 9oz
Barrel22.0in long, 4 grooves, right hand twist
Feed system 10-round detachable box magazine
System of operation Gas; locking flaps
Manufacturers Carl Walther Waffenfabrik, Zella-Mehlis
Berliner-lubecker Maschinenfabrik AG,
Lubeck Gustloffwerke, Suhl

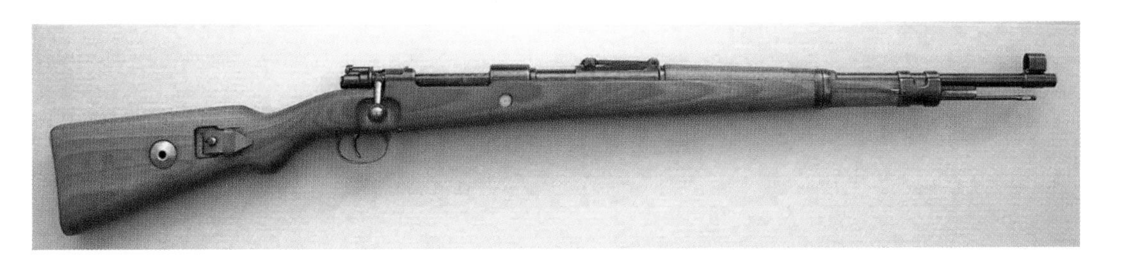

*Karabiner 98K*

## Karabiner 98K

The Karabiner 98K was the last of the long line of Mauser rifles used by the German Army and based on the original Mauser Gewehr 98.

With the adoption of 'short' rifles for the armed forces of both Britain and America, the German Army, called for the development of a short version of the Gew 98, calling it the Karabiner 98; this was slightly confusing, because they had already produced a carbine version and called it the Karabiner 98, but since the new short rifle rapidly replaced the carbine, the anomaly did not last for long. The principal change was, of course, the loss of six inches from the barrel, but the bolt handle was also turned down and the wood of the stock beneath cut away to allow the bolt to be grasped more easily. The rear sight was also simplified. This became the standard infantry weapon during World War I and afterwards completely replaced the Gew 98 rifle; in its postwar version it was re-Christened the Kar 98a.

During the early 1930s one or two small changes were made in the design, largely, as usual, to facilitate mass-production, and the resulting weapon was adopted as the standard rifle for the new Wehrmacht in 1935 as the Kar 98K. It was produced by the million in a number of factories, and production continued until the end of the war in 1945, since the development of automatic rifles never reached the point at which production of bolt-action rifles could be terminated.

Caliber 7.92mm
Length 43.6in
Weight 8lb 9oz
Barrel 23.6in long, 4 grooves, right hand twist
Feed system 5-round integral box magazine
System of operation Mauser turn-bolt
Manufacturers Basically Mauserwerke AG,
but innumerable factories built either rifles or components on a sub-contract basis during the war.

*Maschinenpistole 28*

## MASCHINENPISTOLE 28

The MP28 was developed from the WW1 vintage Bergmann Maschinenpistole 18 , one of the first sub-machine guns to come into use. The principal differences were that the weapon now had selective single shot or automatic fire instead of automatic only; the bolt had a separate firing pin; a new rear sight was fitted; and the magazine entered the left side at 90 degrees instead of 45 degrees as on the MP18.

The Model 28 was developed as a commercial product; and the MP28 was available in virtually whatever calibre the customer desired, and was turned out in 7.63mm Mauser, 9mm Parabellum, 9mm Bergmann-Bayard, .45 Colt and 7.65mm Parabellum. It was also made under license in Belgium by the Ancien Etablissment Pieper of Liege, and in Spain. As a result of this latter manufacture it saw widespread use in the Spanish Civil War , one of the factors leading to the re-evaluation of sub-machine guns by Germany and Russia prior to the outbreak of World War II.

Its use in the German Army was princpally in the early part of the war, since It was a 'traditional' weapon, manufactured by time-honored methods of milling and machining, and not amenable to mass production, and it was soon replaced by weapons of more modern construction. However, it deserves credit for being the gun selected by Britain in 1940 to be the standard British sub-machine gun, and it was copied to make the 'Lanchester', used by the Royal Navy.

Calibre 9mm
Length 32.0in
Weight Weight 8lb 12oz
Barrel 7- 75in long, 6 grooves, right hand twist
Feed system 32-round detachable box
System of operation Blow back, selective fire
Rate of fire (cyclic) 500rpm
Manufacturer C. G. Haenel Waffenfabrik, Suhl

*Maschinenpistole MP40*

## MASCHINENPISTOLE 34 ,35

The MP34 was first taken into use by the German police. It was wooden-stocked and had a barrel jacket perforated with long slots and with a built-in compensator at the muzzle. The cocking handle resembled a rifle bolt and protruded from the rear of the receiver end cap. An unusual feature was that the magazine fed from the right, ejection being to the left, and instead of the magazine protruding at 90 degrees to the axis of the weapon, it was slightly angled forward. A double trigger of peculiar form was fitted; pulling the front trigger gave single shots, but further pressure caused it to bear on the secondary trigger to give automatic fire.

The MP34 was in production for about a year, something like 2000 being made, and in mid-1935 a small number of changes were made in order to simplify production This revised model was known as the MP35. It was available with long or short barrels, the long barrel models often being fitted for a bayonet. In subsequent years these guns were sold in fair numbers to Spain, Sweden, Poland and Ethiopia.

In 1940 the Waffen SS adopted the weapon as their standard sub-machine gun, from then on the entire production went to the waffen SS units. It appears to have been mostly used on the Eastern Front, and the few MP35 specimens which appear in the West generally have SS runes engraved on them.

Calibre 9mm
Length 33.0in
Weight Bib 150z
Barrel 7.75in long, 6 grooves, right hand twist
Feed system 32-round detachable box magazine
System of operation Blow back, selective fire
Rate of fire (cyclic) 650rpm
Manufacturer- Carl Walther Waffenfabrik, Zella-Mehlis
Junker & Ruh AG, Karlsruhe

## MASCHINENPISTOLE 43

During the 1930s the German Army spent some time assessing the basic requirements for an infantry rifle, and they came to the conclusion that the traditional rifle cartridge was unnecessarily large and powerful, since analysis revealed that the vast majority of infantry rifle fire was over short ranges. As a result contracts were placed with Carl Walther and Haenel for the development of rifles based around a short 7.92mm cartridge designed by Polte of Magdeburg. This was of standard caliber and utilized a shortened version of the normal cartridge case, features which simplified production since much of the work could be done on existing machinery.

The resulting weapons were known as the Maschinenkarabiner 42-MkB42(H) and MkB42(W). About 4000 of the Walther and 8000 of the Haenel model were produced in 1942-43 and issued to selected units on the Eastern Front for evaluation. As a result of their reports the Haenel pattern was selected for further development, particularly as far as simplification for mass-production was concerned, and the finalized design was issued as the Machine Pistol 43.

Eventually experience with the first models of the MP43 on the Russian Front led to clamorous demands from the rest of the Army. After initial service trials, fittings for a grenade launcher cup were added to the muzzle, and the designation became MP43/1. In 1944 the designation was changed to MP44, and later, it was again renamed as the Sturmgewehr 44 or Assault rifle, the term which has since become associated with this class of weapon.

Caliber 7.92mm Short
Length 37.0in
Weight 11lb 5oz
Barrel 16.5in long, 4 grooves, right hand twist
Feed system 30-round detachable box magazine
System of operation Gas; tipping bolt
Manufacturers C. G. Haenel Waffen- und Fahrradfabrik, Suhl
B. Giepel GmbH,
Waffenfabrik 'Erma', Erfurt Mauserwerke AG, Oberndorf

## MASCHINENPISTOLE 38

Designed by Berthold Giepel of Ermawerke, the MP38 broke new ground in weapon design by having no wood anywhere in its construction and by having a folding stock. The bolt was driven by a return spring contained in a telescoping tube and it carried a spring-retracted firing pin. The muzzle was threaded to take a blank-firing attachment or a combined muzzle cover and cleaning rod guide, and beneath the barrel was a hook-like steel bar which was to prevent damage to the barrel when firing through the gun-port of an armored vehicle and which was designed to prevent the gun being pulled inadvertently inboard during firing should the gunner lose his footing. For all its innovations the MP38 was still largely made by conventional methods, and while successful it was not really suited to mass-production. The MP38 was therefore critically examined and redesigned to make the maximum use of stampings and welded assemblies. The result was known as the MP40 and replaced the MP38 as the standard sub-machine gun, becoming virtually the German Army's trademark. The principal changes were that the body was of stamped sheet steel, formed and welded; the magazine housing was ribbed instead of plain; while the body top was plain instead of ribbed.

Cailiber 9mm
Length 32.75in
Weight 91b
Barrel 9.75in long, 6 grooves, right hand twist
Feed system 32-round box magazine
System of operation Blow back, automatic only
Rate of fire (cyclic) 500rpm
Manufacturer
Erfurter Maschinenfabrik B.
Giepel GmbH, Erfurt

## MASCHINENPISTOLE EMP

The Ermawerke company entered the sub-machine gun field about 1930, making a gun designed by Herr Heinrich Vollmer and Herr Berthold Giepel and known as the Vollmer sub-machine gun. After some commercial success with this weapon it was slightly redesigned and marketed as the'Erma' MaschinenpistoleModell3 5. This had a long barrel and was fitted to take a bayonet. Then came a shorter model without bayonet fittings, and another with a rifle-type fore-end replacing the front pistol grip of the two earlier designs.

The second model, with the short barrel and forward pistol grip, was produced in the greatest number and was adopted by the German Army in small numbers in 1936 when they were still approaching the sub-machine gun with some caution. This model has a barrel jacket with long slots, a magazine entering from the left, and, its most easily recognized feature, a wooden buttstock, the front end of which is formed into a pistol grip. The mechanism uses a simple bolt but has the return spring carried in a telescoping tube, the unique Vollmer patented design which reappeared on theMP38 and MP40.

Calibre 9mm
Length 35.5in
Weight 9lb 2oz
Barrel 10.0in long, 6 grooves, right hand twist
Feed system 25- or 32-round detachable box megazine
Sysltem of operation Blow back, selective fire
Rate of fire Cyclic) 500rpm
Manufacturer Erfurt Maschinenfabrik B Giepel GmbH (Ermawerke), Erfurt

*Goryunov SG 43*

## Goryunov SG 43

Designed by Peter Maximovitch Goryunov and entering service in 1943. The SG43 utilised an entirely new mechanism and represented the first Soviet departure from Degtyarev's designs. The bolt locks by moving sideways into a recess in the gun body, operated by a conventional gas piston. The feed system is unusually complicated since it has to withdraw the rimmed cartridge from the belt, move it forwards in front of the bolt, and then move it sideways into line with the chamber. In spite of the complexity the system is reliable and foolproof and will continue to work irrespective of the gun's attitude-upright, on it's side, or even upside down-though this is more in the nature of a mechanical curiosity than a useful combat feature. Another feature of the SG is the extreme simplicity of its mechanism; there is for example, only one large spring in the gun. It has been acclaimed by one authority as the most successful air-cooled machine gun ever made with the exception of the American Browning. Certainly the Soviets were satisfied with it, and although it never replaced the Maxim during the war since production could not keep up with the demand, in postwar years it became the standard medium gun and also became the standard tank machine gun.

Calibre 7.62mm
Length 44.1in
Weight 30Ib 4oz
Barrel 28.3in long, 4 grooves, right hand .
Feed system Metallic link belt
System of operation
Gas; side-moving bolt
Rate of fire 600rpm
Manufacturer State Arsenals

## Granatwerfer 34

Largely based on the British Stokes mortar of WW1 vintage, the 8cm Schwere Granatwerfer 34 was a conventional design but with a few variations. It was standard equipment in all rifle companies, two mortars being held in the 'Granatwerfergruppe'. On the march the mortar was usually carried in a light horse-drawn cart, in action the three basic sections were carried by the members of the detachment, together with 21 rounds of ammunition.

Variant

8cm Kurz GrW 42 or 'Stummelwerfer' This was a shortened lightweight version; it used the same ammunition but had the barrel length reduced to 29.4in, and had the base plate and bipod lightened and simplified. The total weight was reduced to 62lbs and the maximum range dropped to 1200 yards. Originally developed for air-borne troops, it was later taken into use by all infantry and largely replaced the standard model. The loss of range was compensated for by easier handling.

Calibre 81.4mm
Barrel 45in long, smoothbore
Weight
Barrel 40.3Ib
Bipod 40lb
Base plate 44lb
In action 125lb
Firing mechanism Drop
Elevation 40-90 degrees
Traverse 9 to 15 degrees, varying with elevation
Projectile & weight HE 7lb 8oz Maximum range 2625yds
Rate of fire 15rpm

## Granatwerfer 36

The 5cm mortar was part of the equipment of every German rifle platoon at the out-break of war; it was handled by a three-man squad who carried the mortar and 45 rounds of ammunition between them.

The Granatwerfer 36 was typical of the equipment of the prewar Wehrmacht; a well-designed weapon, well-made of the best materials and immaculately finished. The barrel was attached to the base plate by a locking pin and could be levelled independently of the base plate's orientation. A quick-release gear allowed elevation to be set rapidly, and even a cleaning rod formed part of the basic equipment clipped to the base plate. For long-distance carriage the locking pin was removed and the elevating gear disconnected, so that the barrel and elevating screw became one load and the base plate and levelling base a second load. For short moves in action the whole assembly could be lifted and carried by a handle provided on the barrel.

The first issues were provided with a collimating sight, but as with the British 2in, this was dispensed with in due course, aiming being a matter of the firer's experience. Mortars issued after mid-1938 were never provided with sights.

The 5cm mortar appears to have declined in importance in the German Army much as it did with the Soviets, and it became less used as the war continued, being largely superseded by the Granatwerfer 34.

Calibre 50mm
Barrel 19.3in long, smoothbore Weight in action 30.9lb
Firing mechanism Trip
Elevation 42-90 degrees
Traverse 17 degrees right or left Projectile & weight HE 1lb 15.5oz Maximum range 500m
Rate of fire 40rpm

*Heckler & Koch G3*

## Heckler & Koch G3

The G3 was the culmination of a designed originated by CETME of Spain. Heckler & Koch handled the final development, and the resultant roller-delayed blowback breech system has featured in almost every other Heckler & Koch weapon made since. Adopted in 1959, the G3 has armed the German Army for many years. It was made under license in 13 countries including Mexico, Portugal, Greece, Turkey, Pakistan, Norway, Greece and Saudi Arabia and has served with the armed forces of over 60 countries. There are variant models with short barrels, fixed or folding butts, and there are also variations in the licence-produced models of some countries, but these are generally minor.

CARTRIDGE 7.62 x 51mm NATO

DIMENSIONS
Length, fixed butt: 1025mm (40.35in)
Weight: 4.40kg (7lb 9oz) Barrel: 450mm (l7.71in)
Rifling: 4 grooves, rh Magazine capacity: 20 rounds Rate of fire: 550 rds/min

IN PRODUCTION 1964-

*Heckler & Koch G11*

## Heckler & Koch G11

Development of the G11 began in the 1960s. This revolutionary weapon was intended to become the German Army's standard rifle, but in the 1980s the programme was cancelled due to economic and NATO standardisation factors. However a limited number were issued to Special Forces. It uses entirely different principles to any other firearm and fires a special caseless cartridge. This was developed by Dynamite Nobel and consists of a block of explosive with a bullet buried inside it. The mechanism moves back and forth in recoil inside the outer plastic casing, the amount of recoil varying with the type of fire selected. Although of peculiar appearance and advanced concept, official evaluation proved the G11 to be an excellent weapon.

CARTRIDGE
4.7 x 33mm caseless

DIMENSIONS (G36)
Length, o/a: 750mm (29.52in)
Weight: 3.65kg (81b 1oz) Barrel: 540mm (21.26in) Rifling: 6 grooves, rh Magazine capacity- 50 rounds Rate of fire: 600 rds/min

IN PRODUCTION
Not applicable

*Heckler & Koch G36*

## HECKLER & KOCH G36

The G36 assault rifle was created at the HK-50 project in the early 1990s. In 1999 when the G11 program collapsed the German Army was left without a 5.56mm rifle to conform to NATO standard, and the G36 was selected as their new standard rifle to replace the G3. In this design H&K abandoned their well-tried roller-locked delayed blow back system and adopter a gas-operated rotating bolt mechanism. The layout is conventional, with the gas cylinder beneath the barrel, a pistol grip, box magazine, and folding tubular butt. A raised sight block at the rear of the receiver carries a 3x optical sight, and the integral carrying handle runs from this block to the front end of the aperture for the line of sight. The cocking handle is underneath the carrying handle and also acts as a bolt closing assist if needed.. An export version, the G36E is also available; this differs only in the optical sight, the G36E having a 1.5x telescope. A carbine version, the G36K is also produced.

CARTRIDGE 5-56 x 45mm NATO

DIMENSIONS (G36)
Length, butt extended: 998mm (39.29in)
Length, butt folded: 758mm (29.84in)
Weight: 3.43kg (7lb 9oz) Barrel: 480mm (l8.89in)
Rifling: 6 grooves, rh Magazine capacity: 30 rounds Rate of fire: 750 rds/min

DIMENSIONS (G36K)
Length, butt extended;858mm (33.78in)
Length, butt folded: 613mm (24.13in)
Weight: 3.13kg (61b 14oz) Barrel: 320mm (12.60in) Rifling: 6 grooves, rh Magazine: 30-rounds
Rate of fire: 750 rds/min

IN PRODUCTION 1995-

*Heckler & Koch G41*

## Heckler & Koch G41

The H&K G41 was designed as an improved HK33 specifically for the NATO standard 5.56mm cartridge. It incorporated the low-noise bolt-closing device first used in the PSG1 sniping rifle, and has a dust cover on the ejection port, and a hold-open device that keeps the bolt open when the magazine is emptied. The G41 uses the NATO-standard magazine interface, capable of accepting M16 and similar magazines. It also has a NATO-standard sight mount for day or night optical sights, and may be fitted with a bipod There is also a folding-butt model.

CARTRIDGE 5.56 x 45mm NATO

DIMENSIONS (G36)
Length, o/a: 997mm (39.25in)
Weight: 4.10kg (91b 1oz) Barrel: 450mm (17.71in) Rifling: 6 grooves, rh Magazine capacity: 30 rounds Rate of fire: 850 rds/min

IN PRODUCTION 1983-

*Heckler & Koch HK53*

## Heckler & Koch HK21

Designed by Heckler and Koch of Obendorf-Neckar, and now a subsidiary of British Aerospace, the HK21 was designed as a general-purpose machine gun, capable of being used on a bipod or tripod, to accompany the G3 rifle. It is much the same as the rifle but with a heavier barrel which can quickly be changed and is belt-fed. However, it is possible to remove the belt-feed mechanism and replace it with a magazine adapter, using the G3 rifle magazine. It could also be converted to 5.56 x 45mm or 7.62 x 39mm calibres by changing the barrel, belt feed plate and bolt, making it a very versatile design. It was adopted by Portugal, and some African and South-East Asian countries in the 1970s and many are still in use. It was replaced in production by the HK21A1, an improved model and then by the present HK21E which has a three-round burst facility and various other improvements. There is also 5.56mm version of the HK21E, the HK23E and a magazine fed versions of the 21E and 23E known as the HK11E and HK13E respectively.

CARTRIDGE 7.62 x 51mm NATO

DIMENSIONS
Length o/a: 1021mm (40.2in) Weight: 792kg (17lb 7oz) Barrel: 450mm (17.71in) Rifling: 4 grooves, rh
Feed system: belt
Rate of fire: 900 rds/min

IN PRODUCTION 1970-

*Heckler & Koch HK33*

## Heckler & Koch HK33

Essentially the standard G3 modified to 5.56mm calibre; the HK33's mechanical operation is exactly the same, as is its outline. Several parts are common, but interchanging parts is not to be recommended as some parts are different, though they may look and fit in apparently the same way in both weapons. There is a fixed butt model and also a short-barrelled carbine version known as the HK33K E. There was also an HK33SGI sniper version, with special sight mount and telescope sight, and the fixed butt model can be found with a bipod, It has been used by Chile, Brazil, Malaysia and Thailand and various other forces in SE Asia and South America.

CARTRIDGE
5.56 x 45mm NATO or M193

DIMENSIONS
Length, stock extended: 940mm (37.0in)
Length, stock folded: 735mm (28.94in)
Weight: 365kg (8lb 1oz) Barrel: 390mm (1535in)
Rifling: 6 grooves, rh Magazine capacity: 25 rounds Rate of fire: 750 rds/min

IN PRODUCTION 1968-

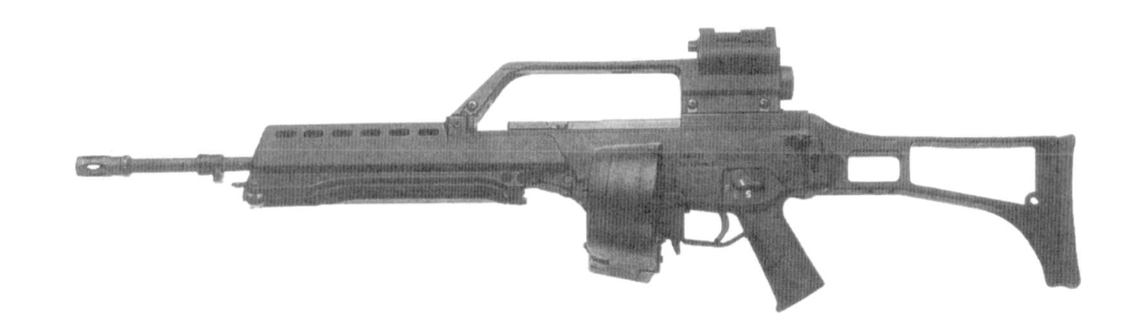

*Heckler & Koch MG36*

## Heckler & Koch MG36

The MG36 is the latest light machine gun design from Heckler & Koch and is derived from the G36 rifle, and like that weapon breaks with the H&K delayed blowback tradition by being gas operated. It is a light weight, compact weapon making extensive use of composite materials in its construction. It has a heavier barrel than the G36, and is fitted with a bipod, but apart from these features it is precisely the same as the rifle. A variant mode, the MG36E, is offered for export; it differs from the German service G36 only in the optical sight, which offers 1.5x magnification instead of 3x.

CARTRIDGE 5.56 x 45mm

DIMENSIONS
Length o/a: 998mm (39.29in) Weight: 3.58kg (7lb 4oz) Barrel: 480mm (18.9in) Rifling: 6 grooves, rh
Magazine capacity: 30-round box or 100-round dual-drum 'Beta-C' magazine
Rate of fire: 750 rds/min

IN PRODUCTION 1995 -

*Heckler & Koch MP5*

## Heckler & Koch MP5

The Heckler & Koch MP5 is the most widely employed and distributed submachine gun of recent decades and is still in production in Germany and several other nations, including the USA, Greece, Pakistan and Turkey. Unlike other submachine guns the MP5 employs the Heckler & Koch roller-delayed blow back breech mechanism as employed on the G3 automatic rifle. Numerous variants have been produced with both fixed and telescopic butt stocks. At least 20 sub-variants have been produced but they all have the same basic receiver and mechanism. Barrel lengths may vary. Some models have combined safety and selector switches that cater for burst fire limiting devices, while others fire semi-automatic only. Versions have been produced for the US market chambered for 10mmAuto or .40 S&W but most models fire 9 x 19mm. There are models with straight and curved magazines.

CARTRIDGE
9 x 19mm Parabellum

DIMENSIONS (fixed butt) Length o/a: 680mm (26.75in) Barrel: 225mm (8.85in) Weight. 2.54kg (5lb 9oz) Rifling:. 6 grooves, rh Magazine capacity: 15 or 30 rounds
Rate of Fire: 800 rds/min

IN PRODUCTION 1966

*Heckler & Koch MP5K*

## Heckler & Koch MP5K

This is a special short version of the MP5 intended for use by police and anti-terrorist squads who require very compact firepower. Mechanically it is the same as the MP5 but with a shorter barrel and smaller magazines. Four versions are made; the MP5K is fitted with adjustable iron sights or a telescope if desired; the MP5KA1 has a smooth upper surface with very small iron sights so that there is little to catch in clothing or a holster in a quick draw; the MP5KA4 is similar to the MP5K but has an additional three-round burst facility; and the MP5KA5 is similar to the A1 with the addition of the three-round burst facility. No butt is fitted, but there is a robust front grip that gives good control when firing.

CARTRIDGE
9 x 19mm Parabellum

DIMENSIONS
Length o/a: 325mm (12.67in) Barrel: 115mm (4.5in) Weight: 199kg (4lb 6oz) Rifling: 6 grooves, rh Magazine capacity: 15 or 30 rounds Rate of Fire: 900 rds/min

IN PRODUCTION 1972

*Heckler & Koch MP5SKO PDW*

## Heckler & Koch MP5SKO PDW

This was designed by the Heckler & Koch subsidiary in the USA as a personal defence weapon for aircrew and vehicle-borne troops who need a compact form of fire power. It is, in effect, the MP5K fitted with a folding butt and with the muzzle modified to accept a silencer There is also provision for fitting a laser spot projector. Should the butt not be needed, it can easily be removed and a butt cap fitted on the end of the receiver. Selective fire is standard, but a two or three round burst unit can be fitted to the mechanism if required.

CARTRIDGE
9 x 19mm Parabellum

DIMENSIONS
Length, with butt-cap: 349mm (13.75in)
Length, with butt extended: 603mm (23.75in)
Length, with butt folded: 368mm (14.50in)
Barrel: 127mm (5.0in)
Weight with butt: 2.79kg (6lb 2oz)
Weight with butt-cap: 209kg (4lb 10oz)
Rifling: 6 grooves, rhMagazine capacity: 30-rounds Rate of Fire: 900 rds/min

IN PRODUCTION 1991

*Heckler & Koch MP5SD*

## HECKLER & KOCH MP5SD

This is the silenced member of the MPS family; the mechanism is exactly the same as the standard MP5 but the short barrel is drilled with 30 holes and surrounded by a large silencer casing. This casing is divided into two chambers; the first surrounds the barrel and receives the propellant gas via the 30 holes, which also serve to reduce the bullet's velocity to below the speed of sound. The gas flow is broken up in this chamber to dissipate some of the velocity and heat, and then pass to the second expansion chamber before being released to the atmosphere.

There are six versions of this weapon; the MP5SDl has the end of the receiver closed by a cap and has no butt-stock; the SD2 has a fixed plastic butt; the SD3 has a sliding retractable butt; all three can fire either single shots or automatic. The SD4 is as for the SDl but with the addition of a three-round burst facility; the SDS is the SD2 with three-round burst; and the SD6 is the SD3 with three-round burst.

CARTRIDGE
9 x 19mm Parabellum

DIMENSIONS SD1
Length o/a: 550mm (21.65in) Barrel: 146mm (5.75in) Weight: 2.9kg (6lb 6oz) Rifling: 6 grooves, rh Magazine capacity: 15 or 30 rounds Rate of Fire: 800 rds/min

IN PRODUCTION 1970

*Heckler & Koch PSG1*

## Heckler & Koch PSG1

The PSG1 is a high-precision sniping rifle using the standard H&K roller-locked delayed blow back breech system with a special long and heavy barrel. It was designed from the outset as a highly specialised sniper rifle, input was sought from various prospective special forces customers such as GSG9 and the SAS. The result is one of the most accurate and expensive sniper rifles available. The trigger unit can be removed from the pistol grip, and can be adjusted for pull. The stock is fully adjustable in all directions so that every individual can fit the weapon to his own stance. No iron sights are fitted; a NATO standard mounting is built into the receiver top and the rifle is always issued with 6 x 42 telescope with illuminated graticule although a claw fitting is also available to allow virtually any scope to be mounted.

CARTRIDGE 7.62 x 51mm NATO

DIMENSIONS
Length o/a: 1208mm (47.55in) Weight: 8.10kg (17lb 13oz) Barrel: 650mm (25.6in)
Rifling: 4 grooves, rh
Magazine capacity: 5 or 20 rounds

IN PRODUCTION 1975 -

## Hughes Chain Gun EX34

The EX34 was developed by Hughes Helicopters and Ordnance Systems, Culver City California USA The Chain Gun derives its name from the use of a conventional roller chain in an endless loop that drives the bolt. The chain is driven by an electric motor, and a dynamic brake on the motor ensures that when the trigger is released the bolt stops in the open position, so that there is no danger of ammunition cook-off. The motor drives the belt independently of the bolt mechanism so that there is ample power to handle long belts. The Chain Gun is particularly well suited to tank installation since case ejection is forward, under control, and the relatively long bolt closure dwell time reduces the amount of fumes released into the vehicle. The Hughes Chain Gun is one of the few new operating principles which have appeared in recent years, and is in use in 25mm calibre in the US M2 Bradley MICV and in 7.62mm calibre on the British 'Warrior' MICV, being manufactured under license in Britain as the L94Al.

CARTRIDGE 7.62 x 51mm NATO

DIMENSIONS
Length o/a: 1250mm (49.21in) Weight: 17.86kg (39lb 6oz) Barrel: 703mm (27.68in) Rifling: 4 grooves, rh
Feed system: disintegrating link belt
Rate of fire: 520 rds/min

IN PRODUCTION 1980 -

## Hungary SMG, Mod 39M

The Model 39M sub-machine gun was designed by P. D. Kiraly of the Danuvia Company during the late 1930s. It is an unusually bulky weapon for a sub-machine gun, fully stocked like a rifle and taking the standard Hungarian Army bayonet. The magazine can be folded forward to lie in a housing slot cut within the wooden fore-end, and when so folded a spring-loaded cover snaps across the feed entry to keep out dirt. The bolt is of two-piece design with an intermediate rocking arm which engages in a recess in the gun body. When fired, the cartridge case sets back against the front, light, section of the bolt, which begins to move to the rear but which must rotate the rocking arm before it can transmit movement to the rear, heavy, section of the bolt and thus allow the whole assembly to begin movement to the rear. This system is necessary on this weapon, since it is chambered for the powerful 9mm Mause cartridge, and some form of delay is essential in order to allow breech pressure to drop in such a long barrel.

The 39M was invariably excellently manufactured of the highest quality materials and was a reliable and accurate weapon. Although called the '39' it appears that production did not get under way until late 1940 and the first issues were made to the Hungarian Army in 1941. The Hungarians fought against the Russians and most of these weapons fell into Soviet hands.

Calibre 9 mm
Length 41.25in
Weight 8lb 3oz
Barrel19.65in long, 6 grooves, right hand twist
Feed system 40-round detachable box magazine
System of operation Delayed blow back, selective fire
Rate of fire (cyclic) 750rpm
Manufacturer Danuvia Waffen und Munitionsfabrik AG, Budapest

## INSAS ASSAULT RIFLE

The INSAS is a gas-operated selective-fire assault rifle that was developed in the mid 1980s. Its design incorporates several features taken from other weapons. The receiver and pistol grip show Kalashnikov influence, the for-end resembles that of the Armalite AR15, and the forward cocking handle is based on the Heckler & Koch rifles these various features have been well combined to produce a well-balanced and effective weapon. An unusual feature is the use of the old Lee-Enfield style butt-plate to provide a trap for the cleaning material and oil bottle. The rifle uses the well-tried operating system of a gas piston driving a bolt carrier and rotating bolt, and the magazine housing has been standardised on the M16 dimensions. The fire selector permits single shots or three-round bursts, but there is no provision for automatic fire. The assault rifle is made in fixed and folding butt versions, and there is also a heavy-barrelled version for use in the squad automatic role. The cartridge is based on the Belgian SS109 but is not to NATO standard

CARTRIDGE
5.56mm x 45mm

DIMENSIONS
Length fixed stock: 945mm (37.20in)Length stock folded. 750mm (29.52in)
Length stock extended 960mm (37.80in)
Weight: 3.20kg (7lbs1oz)Barrel: 464mm (18.27in)
Rifling: 6 grooves rh
Magazine capacity- 22 rounds Cyclic rate: 650 rds/min

IN PRODUCTION 1993

## INSAS

This is the companion weapon to the INSAS (Indian Small Arms System) assault rifle in the Indian army infantry, and is itself, effectively a heavy-barrelled version of the INSAS assault rifle. It is gas-operated, using a rotating bolt, and can deliver single shots or automatic fire. The barrel is heavier than that of the rifle, is chromed internally, and has a different rifling contour to develop better long-range ballistic performance. The weapon is sighted up to 1000 meters. The muzzle is formed to the NATO-standard 22mm diameter for grenade launching, and a bayonet can be fitted. The bipod is the same as that produced in Indian factories for the Bren and Vickers Berthier machine guns during World War Two. The INSAS is in service with the Indian army.There is also a Para version with a folding stock and a slightly shorter barrel for use by airborne troops.

CARTRIDGE 5.56 x 45mm

DIMENSIONS
Length: 1050mm (41.34in) Weight: unloaded 6.23kg (13lb 11oz)
Barrel: 535mm (21.06in)Rifling: 4 grooves, rh
Magazine capacity: 30 rounds Rate of fire- 650 rds/min

IN PRODUCTION

*Ingram Model 10*

## Ingram Model 10

Designed by Gordon Ingram as cheap submachine gun with extremely high rate of fire, and intended to use the very effective Sionics Company sound suppressor. The Model 10 is of mainly pressed steel construction and manufactured to the high standards necessary to cope with the forces generated by the high rate of fire. It has a folding steel stock and the the silencer is coated in heat-resistant plastic to enable it to be used as fore-grip. Something like 10,000 of these guns were produced and supplied to US police forces, US Army, Cuba and Peru, and it was also made under licence in Peru. Most were in 45 ACP calibre, though some were also made in 9mm Parabellum and in .38 Super Auto chambering.

CARTRIDGE .45 ACP

DIMENSIONS .45in model
Length, stock extended: 548mm (21.575in)
Length, stock retracted: 269mm (10.95in)
Barrel: 146mm (5.75in) Weight, loaded: 3.818kg (81b 6oz)
Rifling: 6 grooves, rh Magazine capacity: 30 rounds Rate of fire: 1,145 rds/min

IN PRODUCTION 1949-52

## Beretta, Model 1938A

This weapon originated as a semi-auto-automatic carbine in 1935, but was then reworked to become a selective-fire weapon and went into production in 1938. A highly successful weapon, it underwent various minor modifications during its life but remained in production until 1950 before being superseded by more modern designs. The first model was fully stocked, had the magazine below the weapon, a folding bayonet of special design, and had a cooling jacket with long slots surrounding the barrel. It also had an entirely new firing mechanism with two triggers; the front trigger for firing single shots, and the rear trigger for firing automatic. The front end of the barrel jacket was formed into a rudimentary compensator with two large holes in its top. Although quite a serviceable design, this was only produced in small numbers during 1938 and was soon replaced by the second version, which has no distinctive model number. This version added a fire selector lever in the shape of a cross-bolt locking bar behind the rear trigger which, when pushed in, prevented the rear trigger being depressed and thus restricted fire to single shots. The barrel jacket had smaller , circular holes, but the compensator and bayonet of the first model were retained.

Calibre 9mm
Length 37.Sin
Weight 91b 4oz
Barrel12.5in long, 6 grooves, right hand twist
Feed system 10-, 20-, 30-, or 4Q-round detachable box magazines
System of operation Blow back, selective fire
Rite of fire (cyclic) 600rpm
Manufacturer P. Beretta, Brescia

## FNAB-43 sub-machine gun

This little-known weapon was designed and developed in Italy during the war and manufactured during 1943 and 1944. It is believed that not more than about 7000 were made, and they were all issued to Italian and German units fighting in Northern Italy.

It was an unusual weapon, one of the more remarkable things about it being that its design was such as to call for expensive and time-consuming methods of precision engineering at a time when the general tendency was to make weapons-particularly sub-machine guns-as cheap and simple as possible. This doubtless accounts for the small production figures; nevertheless it was a well made and efficient weapon.

Other features of this weapon included a muzzle brake and compensator built into the barrel casing in the manner of some Russian weapons, and a magazine housing which is hinged so that the magazine can lie beneath the barrel.

Calibre 9 mm
length 31.15in
Weight 8lb 12oz
Barrel 7.Bin long, 6 grooves, right hand twist
Feed system 20- or 40-round detachable box magazine
System of operation Delayed blow back, selective fire
Rate of fire (cyclic) 400rpm
Manufacturer Fabrica Nazionale d'armes, Brescia

*Mannlicher Modello 91*

## Mannlicher Modello 91

This basic Italian army rifle was developed at the Turin Army Arsenal in 1890.

On the whole the MI891 was a serviceable enough weapon and on a par with its contemporaries, and it served as a basis for a host of variations over the years. Its principal drawback was the weak 6.5mm cartridge that it fired; the Italians became aware of this deficiency and in 1938 introduced a 7 .35mm cartridge which they hoped would replace the 6.5mm. Unfortunately the planned change of calibre never took place to the extent hoped for. A small number of rifles and carbines in 7.35mm were eventually issued, but the 6.5mm weapons were by far the most common throughout the whole of the war.

Caliber 6.5mm
Length 50.79in
Weight Bib 6oz
Barrel30.71in long, 4 grooves, right hand twist
Feed system 6-round integral box magazine, clip-loaded
System of operation Turnbolt
Manufacturer State Arsenals

*TZ-45*

## TZ-45

Another Italian wartime design produced in small numbers by a small company, the TZ-45 is much more the sort of weapon one would expect in that place and at that time. It was cheaply made from metal stampings, welded together in parts, and the finish is rudimentary, but, more importantly it worked. A muzzle compensator is fitted, and the shoulder stock is formed of steel rods which slide alongside the receiver when retracted. Two separate safety systems are fitted; the fire selector lever has a 'safe' position which locks the bolt in either the forward or rearward positions, while a grip safety is fitted behind the
magazine housing. Unless the weapon is held properly and this grip compressed, the bolt cannot move in either direction to cock or to fire.
The entire issue of the TZ-45 appears to have gone to various units of the Italian Army operating against guerrilla forces in the mountains, and no more than 6000 were made during 1944-45.

Calibre 9 mm
length 33.5in
Weight 71b 3oz
Barrel gin long, 6 grooves, right hand twist
Feed system 40-round detachable box magazine
System of operation Blow back, selective fire
Rate of fire (cyclic) 550rpm
Manufacturer Tonone et Zorzola, Gardoneval-Trompe, Italy

## Japan 90mm Mortar, Type 94

The Type 94 was a heavy and complex weapon, a surprising piece of equipment to find in the Japanese Army where simplicity and lightness were the usual keynotes. But due to its massiveness, and particularly to its very effective recoil system, it was an outstandingly successful and effective weapon. However, it was relatively uncommon, and there do not appear to have been very large numbers manufactured.

The general design of the weapon was conventional, except for the inclusion of two hydro-pneumatic recoil cylinders. These were attached to a U-shaped yoke which rested on the base plate. The lower end of the barrel was attached to a cross-piece which in turn was attached to the lower end of the recoil cylinders. The piston rods of the recoil system were attached to the barrel band and also to two spring shock-absorbers at the top of the bipod.

In addition to the customary high explosive bomb, this weapon fired an unusual incendiary bomb containing white phosphorus, carbon disulphide and about 40 pellets impregnated with the incendiary composition. A small explosive charge in the nose served to burst the shell and scatter the contents. This projectile appears to have rarely been used during the war, and was apparently developed for use in China in the 1930s.

Calibre 90mm
Barrel 47.8in long, smoothbore
Weight Barrel 74.5Ib
Bipod 73lb
Recoil system 104lb
Base plate 88.5Ib
In action 340lb
Firing mechanism Drop
Elevation 45-70 degrees
Traverse 10 degrees
Projectile & weight HE 11.5Ib
Maximum range 4050yds
Rate of fire 15rpm

## Arisaka rifle, Meiji 38

Based on the Mauser and designed by a commission headed by Colonel Arisaka, the Meiji 38 model was introduced in 1905 (38th year of the Meiji reign), replacing the. original 1897 model and displaying one or two improvements over it. The mechanism is basically Mauser but with a large mushroom-headed safety knob at the rear end of the bolt, which in turn led to a redesign of the striker mechanism. An unusual addition, though rarely found on specimens today, was a sheet-metal bolt cover which reciprocated with the bolt but served to keep rain and dust out of the mechanism. While it did all that was claimed, like most other devices of asimilar nature it was flimsy and prone to rattle at inopportune moments, giving away the owner's location, and the vast majority were 'lost in action' at the earliest oppolrtunity.

Between the Wars, the Japanese came to the conclusion that their elderly 6.5mm ridge was no longer efficient, and in 1930s they developed a 7.7mm round to replace it. They also developed a rifle to fire it, which was little more than a re-barrelled Model 38. However, manufacturing problems prevented more than a few of these rifles reached the hands of troops. As a result the 6.5mm round and its associated rifle remained the standard throughout the war.

Callber 6.5mm
Length 50.25in
Weight 91b 8oz
Barrel 31.45in long, 6 grooves, right hand twist
Feed system 5-round integral box magazine
System of operation Mauser turnbolt
Manufacturer State Arsenals

## SUB-MACHINE GUN, TYPE 100

There was little in the way of sub-machine gun development in Japan until about 1935, after which an experimental model was produced and tested. But there appears to have been little enthusiasm for the weapon,in spite of the fact that the sub-machine gun would have been an ideal weapon for theJapanese Army and could well have effected the outcome of some of the conflicts in the Pacific . The Type 100, Model 1940, was issued in 1941-42 in limited numbers. Although far from perfect its performance was good enough to stimulate interest in the weapon, and this led to development of an improved version, the Model 1944, but work began too late and was carried out too slowly to allow stocks to be built up. The Model 40 came in two patterns, one for infantry use with a solid stock and one for Airborne troops using a hinged folding stock. Both were fitted with bayonet bars under the barrel, and the interior of the barrels was chrome plated. The infantry models were sometimes fitted with a small bipod. The only recorded use of these weapons in combat was in the Japanese parachute attack on the Dutch oilfields in Java in 1942, when they were reported to have been highly effective. There is no record of their appearance against US forces in the South Pacific nor against British troops in Burma. It is believed that less than 10,000 of both models were produced.

Calibre 8 mm
Length 35.0in
Weight 8lb 8oz
Barrel9.0in long, 6 grooves, right hand twist
Feed system 30-round detachable box magazine
System of operation Blow back, selective fire
Rate of fire (cyclic) 450rpm
Msnufacturer Atsuta Ordnance Factory,Nagoya Arsenal, Japan

## TYPE 89

The Japanese Defence Agency have designed this rifle to replace the aging Type 64 as the standard Japanese service rifle. Gas-operated, with a rotating bolt, it uses an unusual gas system which ensures a lower initial impulse on the gas piston, so giving a lower felt recoil and prolonging the life of the weapon. A manual safety catch and fire selector is positioned on the right side of receiver above the trigger. This is moved up for safe, down one notch for single shots, down and fully forward for automatic fire. When set at automatic, another catch behind the trigger gives 3-round bursts. The three-round burst facility is an entirely separate mechanism, so that if anything should go wrong with it, the single-shot and automatic functions are not impaired. There is a fixed-butt version as well as the folding butt type, and both models are equipped with a bipod.

CARTRIDGE
5.56mm x 45mm NATO

DIMENSIONSLength stock folded: 570mm (22.44in)
Length stock extended: 916mm (36in)
Weight: 3.50kg (7lbs12oz)Barrel: 420mm (16.54in)
Rifling: 6 grooves rh
Magazine capacity- 20 or 30 rounds Cyclic rate: 750 rds/min

IN PRODUCTION 1990

*Kalashnikov AK-101 & AK-102*

*Johnson, cal .30 rifle, M1941*

## JOHNSON, CAL .30 RIFLE, M1941

This rifle, the last of a series of designs by Captain Melvin M. Johnson, and first serviceable design in first appeared in1936. This was improved still further, and in 1940 the Dutch Government contracted to purchase a number, which gave Johnson the opportunity to go into production.
The Johnson is one of the very few" recoil-actuated rifles to acheive any degree of success. Recoil operation demands , movement of the barrel, which is not a t desirable feature in a shoulder arm; nevertheless the Johnson worked
In 1940 the Dutch Government ordered 50,000 of these rifles for use in the Netherlands East Indies. Before delivery could be completed the Japanese overran the Indies. The balance of the order was then taken over by the United States Marines who were finding it difficult to obtain sufficient M1 Garand rifles for their needs. The Johnson was primarily issued to parachute units, due to its lightness and due also to the fact that it could be rapidly stripped down and stowed about the paratrooper's person.
General concensus of user opinion seems to be that the weapon was not as reliable in action as was hoped. Numerous small modifications were made from time to time, but the design was never really finalized and the rifle was declared obsolete after the war ended.

Caliber .3Oin
Length 45.5in
Weight 91b 8oz
Barrel 22.0in long, 4 grooves, right hand twist
Feed system 10-round rotary integral magazine
System of operation Recoil; rotating bolt
Manufacturer Johnson Automatics Trust Inc., Providence, RI

*Kord 12 70mm HMG*

## KGP 9

Manufactured by Fegyvergyar the KGP 9 was first revealed in the late 1980s and is the standard submachine gun of the Hungarian military and police forces. It is a conventional blow back weapon, mainly constructed from pressed steel components stiffened with castings. It fires from an open bolt, but the bolt carries a floating firing pin and the actual firing is done by a hammer mechanism. An unusual feature is that the standard barrel can be removed and replaced by a longer one, presumably to convert the weapon into a type of carbine with a longer range.

CARTRIDGE
9 x 19mm Parabellum

DIMENSIONS
Length, with butt extended: 615mm (24.21in)
Length, with butt folded: 355mm (13.95in)
Barrel: 190mm (7.48in)
Weight with butt: 2.75kg (6lb 1oz)
Rifling: 6 grooves, rhMagazine capacity: 25-rounds Rate of Fire: 900 rds/min

IN PRODUCTION 1987

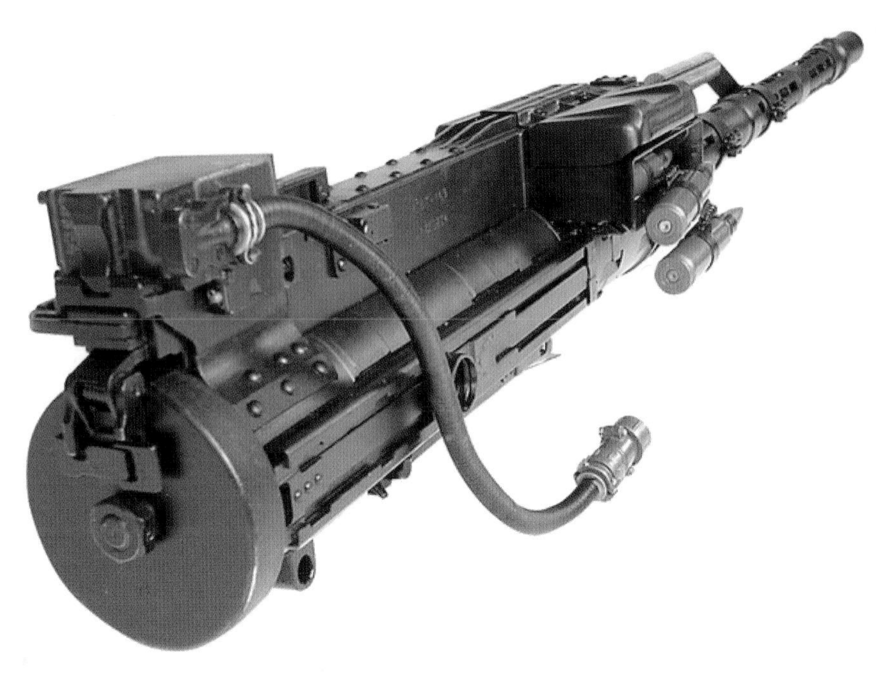

*KPV heavy machine gun*

## KPV HEAVY MACHINE GUN

The world's most powerful machine-gun in large-scale service is the KPV (Krasnoy Pulemet Vladimorova), a weapon development of which began in the USSR in 1944. It fires the Soviet 14.5mm (0.57 in) x 115 cartridge, whose API and HEIT bullets have twice as much energy as a 12.7mm (0.5in) projectile. The KPV is air-cooled with a chromed barrel, and operates on the short recoil system with gas assistance. The bolt is of the rotary type, and the weapon is fed from the left- or right-hand sides by a 40-round belt and has a muzzle velocity of 3,281ft (1000m) per second. The KPV entered service in the late 1940s, and is generally associated with wheeled mountings towed by light vehicles. The standard mountings are the ZPU-1, 2 and -4 carrying one, two or four such weapons, it has also been mounted on a number of AFVs.

CARTRIDGE 14.5 x 115 mm (0.57in) API or HEIT

DIMENSIONS
Length o/a: 2006mm (78.9in) Weight: 49.1kg (108.25lb 6oz) Weight with ZPU-1 mount: 161.5kg (356lb 0oz)
Barrel: 1346mm (53in) Rifling: 4 grooves, rh
Feed system: 40-round belt
Rate of fire: 600 rds/min

*Karabin WZ-35 Marosczekl*

## Karabin WZ-35 Marosczekl

Tthe Poles began development of an anti-tank rifle in the early 1930s, taking the Mauser of 1918 as their starting point. In order to get the highest velocity possible, they pioneered the use of a standard rifle caliber bullet backed by an oversize cartridge, a technique later copied by the Germans. The most notable feature of the Marosczek rifle was its light weight, little more than half the weight of its contemporaries, making it a very handy weapon but giving it a rather fierce recoil, in spite of using an efficient muzzle brake.

In order to achieve the desired high velocity a very energetic and hot propellant was employed, and this led to rapid erosion of the barrel. After 200 rounds had been fired the velocity had fallen to about 3800ft/sec and the penetration performance had deteriorated in proportion. Penetration was helped by adopting a bullet with a tungsten carbide core, and their effective use during the short Polish campaign in 1939 led to the development of similar bullets in Germany and Russia.

Although known as the Model 35, general issue did not commence until early in 1937 and that less than a thousand rifles had been manufactured before the outbreak of war. Such weapons as were serviceable after the defeat were taken into use by the German Army for a short time, until the general use of anti-tank rifles was abandoned.

Caliber 7.92mm
Length 70.0in
Weight 19.5Ib
Barrel 47.25in long, 4 grooves, right hand twist
Feed system 10-round detachable box magazine
System of operation Bolt action
Muzzle velocity 4200ft/sec
Penetration 20mmf300m/0 degrees Manufacturer
Fabryca Brony Radomu (State Arsenal)

*LAW80*

## LAW80

The LAW80 is a one shot, low cost, disposable short-range anti-tank weapon system. It is designed to permit the operator to engage main battle tanks over short ranges with a high probability of a hit.

It is stored and transported in a case holding 24 launchers and is issued directly to the user; it is fully man-portable with personal weapons and pack, and is provided with carrying handles and a shoulder sling.

A spotting rifle is used with the system, which contains five rounds. These can be fired without revealing position. The 9mm ammunition is ballistically matched to the main projectile, and is marked by tracer and a flash head to show a hit on target. The operator can fire the main projectile at any time.

The LAW80 sight has its own sliding protective cover. End caps provide sealing for the tubes against immersion, despite the fact that the round itself is sealed. After removal of the end caps, the HEAT projectile is extended rearwards from the outer tube. The launch tube is automatically locked into position and the sight erected. The gunner then selects 'arm' on a lever to fire either the spotting rifle or the projectile. A non-electrical system consisting of a percussion cap in the launcher, connected by a flash tube to the rocket igniter, fires the projectile. In the British forces the LAW80 is used by the infantry, support arms, Royal Marines, RAF Regiment and Special Forces.

Origin: UK
Type: Portable anti-tank weapon
Dimensions: Length 3.3ft (1m) folded; 4.95ft (1.5m) extended.
Calibre: 3.7in (94mm)
Weights: carrying 21.1 lb (9.6kg), firing 19.3 lb (8.8kg)
Penetration: More than 2.4in (600mm) of armour
Range: 22-546yds (20-500m)

## LMPW AT 4

The AT-4 is currently in production and has largely replaced the ubiquitous M72A1, as the US Army's infantry squad anti-armour/close support weapon. The M72A1 LAW is now getting very old and is not considered capable of defeating the latest Soviet tank armour. First deliveries began in 1989, direct from FFV of Sweden, but Alisant Techsystems Inc, Minnetonkia, MN, has now begun licensed production at the Joliet Army Ammunition Plant in Illinois.

Type: Single shot, throwaway, squad anti-tank rocket. Calibre: 84mm
Dimensions: Length 39.7in (1008mm)
Launch weight: Complete unit 14.6lb (6.62kg).
Guidance: Iron sights.
Range: over 328 yards (over 300 m).
Muzzle Velocity: 951.4ft/s (290m/s).
Warhead: Fin-stabilized, HE-shaped.

## Lahti-Saloranta, M1926

Aimo Lahti was a well-known Finnish designer and this light machine gun is one of the better inter-war designs. Although it was purchased for evaluation by many countries only the Finns adopted it in quantity, but a modified version for use by aircraft observers was tested by the Royal Air Force in 1934. The Lahti was one of the few recoil-operated light weapons to achieve success, and deserves credit for being probably the only one to be successful in combat-though that may be due to the particular combat. It was used in the Russo-Finnish Winter War of 1939-40, in conditions of extreme dry cold, and Lahti's designs all exhibit a concern for protecting the weapon from dust and dirtl. The Lahti action relies on the recoil of the barrel on firing; this carries both barrel and breech block to the rear, locked together until the chamber pressure has dropped to a safe level. At this point the barrel stops, the block is unlocked and allowed to continue rear wards to complete the loading and cocking cycle. While there is much more mechanical movement going on than in the ordinary gas-operated light machine gun, the action is rather more smooth and thus the disturbance of aim is no worse than with other systems.

Little is known of the use or effects of the Lahti during the Winter War, but since the Finns put up a good fight, in spite of the fact that the Soviet Army outnumbered the Finnish Army by an enormous ratio, and since they retained the Lahti in service until the late 1940s, it appears to have been satisfactory.

Calibre 7.62mm
Length 46.5in
Weight 19lb
Barrel 22.3in long, 4 grooves, right hand twist
Feed system 20-round detachable box or 75-round detachable drum
System of operation Recoil
Rate of fire (cyclic) 500rpm
Manufacturer
V KT (Valtion),
Jyvaskylo, Finland

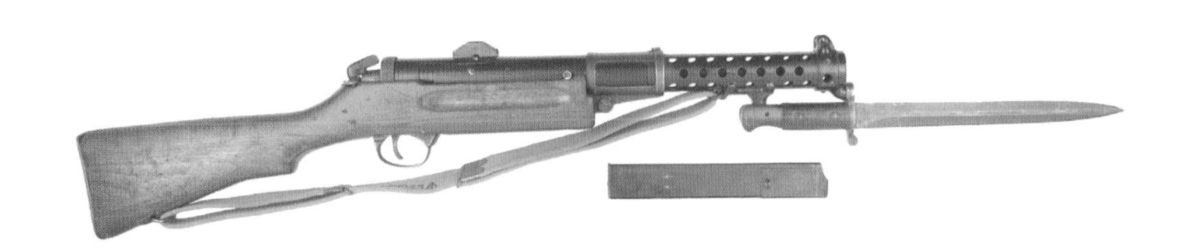

*Lanchester*

## LANCHESTER

In 1940, with the Dunkirk evacuation completed and invasion apparently imminent, the Royal Air Force decided to adopt a sub machine gun for airfield defence. With no time to spare for the development of a new weapon it decided to adopt a direct copy of the German MP 28. The period was so desperate that the Admiralty decided to join the RAF in adopting the new weapon, but in the event it was only the Admiralty which adopted the resultant weapon.

The British copy of the German MP 28 was called the Lanchester after George H. Lanchester, who was charged with producing the weapon at the Sterling Armament Company at Dagenham. The Lanchester emerged from its British development as a sound, sturdy weapon in many ways ideal for use by boarding and raiding parties It was a very solid, soundly engineered piece of weaponry with all the trimmings of a former era.

The Lanchester had a well-machined wooden butt and stock, the blow back mechanism was very well made, of the finest materials, the breech block well machined and the magazine housing was fabricated from solid brass A few typical British design details were added, such as a mounting on the muzzle for a long-blade British bayonet (very useful in boarding party situations), and the rifling differed from that of the German original in details to accommodate the different type of ammunition fired by the Lanchester.

The magazine for the Lanchester was straight and carried a useful load of 50 rounds. Stripping was aided by a catch on top of the receiver, and the first model was the Machine Carbine. 9-mm Lanchester. Mk I capable of single-shot or automatic fire. On the Lanchester Mk 1* this was changed to automatic fire only, and many Mk 1s were converted to Mk 1* standard at Royal Navy workshops. The Lanchester was an unashamed copy of a German design, but gave good service to the Royal Navy throughout and after World War II Many old sailors still speak of the Lanchester with respect but not with affection, for it was a heavy weapon and it had one rather off-putting feature. If the butt was given a hard knock or jar while the gun was cocked and loaded it would fire. The last example left Royal Navy use during the 1960s.

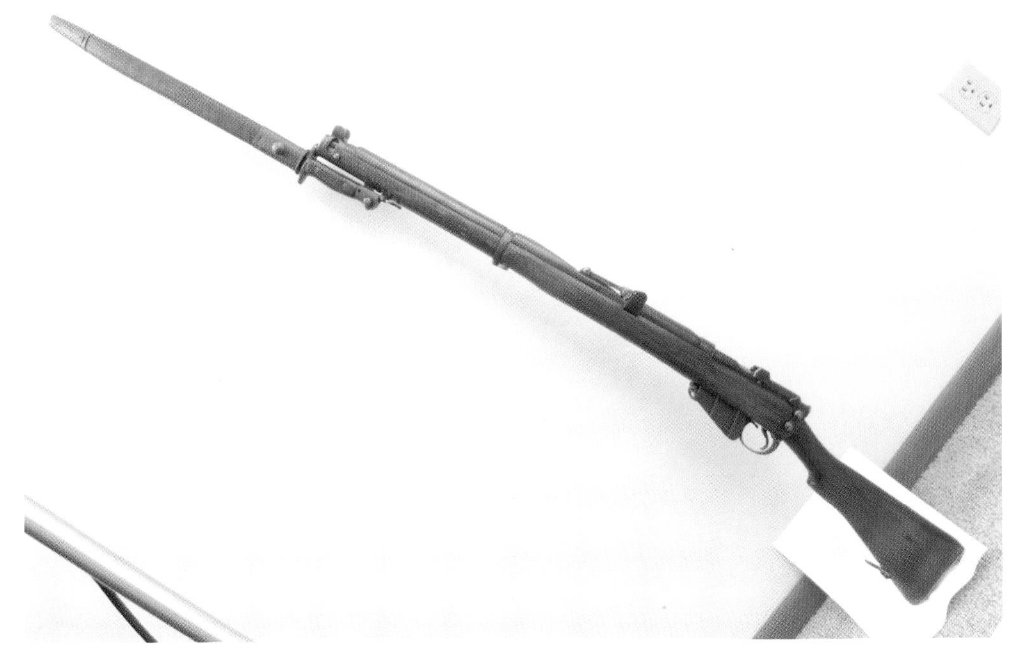

*Lee enfield*

## Lee Enfield

The well-known Lee-Enfield rifle began its service with the British Army in 1895 and ran into some 27 different models before being replaced by a self-loader in 1957. The most famous model was probably the Mark 3, the 'Short' Lee-Enfield, so-called because it introduced a new idea into military rifles. Prior to its introduction, in 1903, it was customary to produce two rifle-type weapons, one a long rifle for infantry use and one a short carbine for cavalry and other mounted troops such as engineers and artillery. The 'Short' Lee-Enfield was shorter than a normal 'long' rifle, and longer than a carbine, and thus it was possible to standardize on one weapon for all branches of the Army.

Between the wars a series of prototypes were produced incorporating various improvements mostly aimed at making the weapon easier to produce. These led finally to the next major production version, which under an new system of nomenclature, became the 'No.4 Markl' , the standard World War II rifle.

The No.4 rifle was much like the earlier Mark 6, but there were numerous small changes which simplified production. It was first issued late in 1939, though not officially adopted until 13 February 1941.Well over a million were made during the war, both in Britain and across the Atlantic in the USA and Canada, and after some misgivings by old soldiers who missed the immaculate finish of the Mark 3, the No.4 became liked and trusted in its turn. It remains in service today as a sniping rifle, using 7.62mm NATO ammunition.

Caliber .303in
Length 44.43in
Weight 91b 1oz
Carrel 25.19in long, 5 grooves, right hand twist
Feed system 10-round detachable box magazine
System of operation Lee turn-bolt Manufacturers
Royal Ordnance Factory, Fazakerley
Royal Ordnance Factory, Maltby Birmingham
Small Arms Co., Tyseley Savage Arms
Corporation, Chicopee Falls, Mass., USA
Long Branch Arsenal, Ontario, Canada

*Lewis*

## Lewis

The Lewis Gun, was an international weapon, for though its origins were American, it was first produced and manufactured in Europe. Its inventor was an American, Samuel McLean, but the basic concept was developed further and promoted by Colonel Isaac Lewis, another American. The US military authorities were unenthusiastic about the new gun, so Lewis took the design to Belgium, where it was put into production for the Belgian army. That was in 1913, and in the following year production was switched to the UK, BSA (Birmingham Small Arms) taking over the programme.

The Lewis Gun was put into production at BSA as the Lewis Gun Mk 1 for the British army for the simple reason that five or six Lewis Guns could be produced in the time it took to produce a single Vickers machine-gun. The fact that the Lewis was light and portable was secondary at that time, but once in service the Lewis proved to be a very popular front-line weapon with a host of mobile tactical uses. The Lewis Gun was one of the first of the true light machine-guns, and with its distinctive overhead drum magazine it was soon a common sight on the British-manned sector of the Western Front.

Only after large numbers of Lewis Guns had been produced in Europe did the USA finally realise the weapon's potential and order it into production for the US Army chambered in the American 0.3-in (7.62-mm) calibre.

Calibre: 0.303in (7.7-mm)
Length overall: 1250 mm (49.2 in)
Weights: 12.25 kg (27Ib)
Barrel: 661 mm (26 in)
Feed: 47 or 97 round overhead drum magazine
Rate of fire, cyclic: 450-500 rpm

*M14 rifle*

## M14 RIFLE

The M14 was a 1950s development of the wartime M1 Garand designed to fire a 7.62mm round to meet NATO standardisation requirements. Initially it was intended to keep the changes to a minimum including a detachable magazine instead of the clip feed and a new barrel of the required calibre and rifling. However at some stage in development a decision was taken make the new weapon an automatic: Provision of automatic fire with a cartridge as heavy as the 7.62 involved strengthening many of the components, and the result was a cumbersome weapon. Most were converted by locking the system at semi-automatic, and with some modifications the weapon was reasonably serviceable. Early models had wooden furniture, then with a glass-fibre hand guard, finally with all synthetic furniture.

CARTRIDGE 762 x 51mm NATO

DIMENSIONS
Length o/a: 1120mm (44.1in) Weight: 5.10kg (11lb 40z) Barrel: 559mm (22.0in)
Rifling: 4 grooves, rh Magazine capacity: 20 rounds Rate of fire: 750 rds/min

IN PRODUCTION 1957-63

*Heckler & Koch HK43 56mm*

*M16 Rifle*

## M16 Rifle

The original M16 was created by the designer Eugene Stoner and was derive from the Armalite AR-10, a revolutionary rifle developed in the mid-50s. The new weapon, known as the Armalite AR-15, was submitted for competitive trials to select the new US service rifle. The AR-15 was selected and standardised as the M16 but not until after the British army had placed an order for 10,000. The Colt Firearms Company were contracted to produce the US armies M16s and, after experience in the field suggested a few improvements, the modified M16A1 took its place on the production lines. Although the M16 will forever be synonymous with the Vietnam War, over three million have been produced and they have seen service with armed forces all round the world.

In the 1980s a new model was introduced the M16A2 the main change was the provision of a new barrel rifled to accept not only the existing ammunition but also the new NATO standard SS109-type M855 round that offered increased range and penetration. At the same time the opportunity was taken to make minor improvements to the handgrip and to fit a burst-limiter to restrict automatic fire to three-round bursts.

CARTRIDGE 5.56 x 45mm NATO
SS109-type M855

DIMENSIONS M16A2
Length o/a: 1006mm (39.63in)Barrel: 508mm (20.0in)Weight: 3.99kg (8lb 12oz) Rifling: 6 grooves rh Magazine: 30 rounds
Cyclic Rate of Fire: 800 rds/min

IN PRODUCTION 1961 -

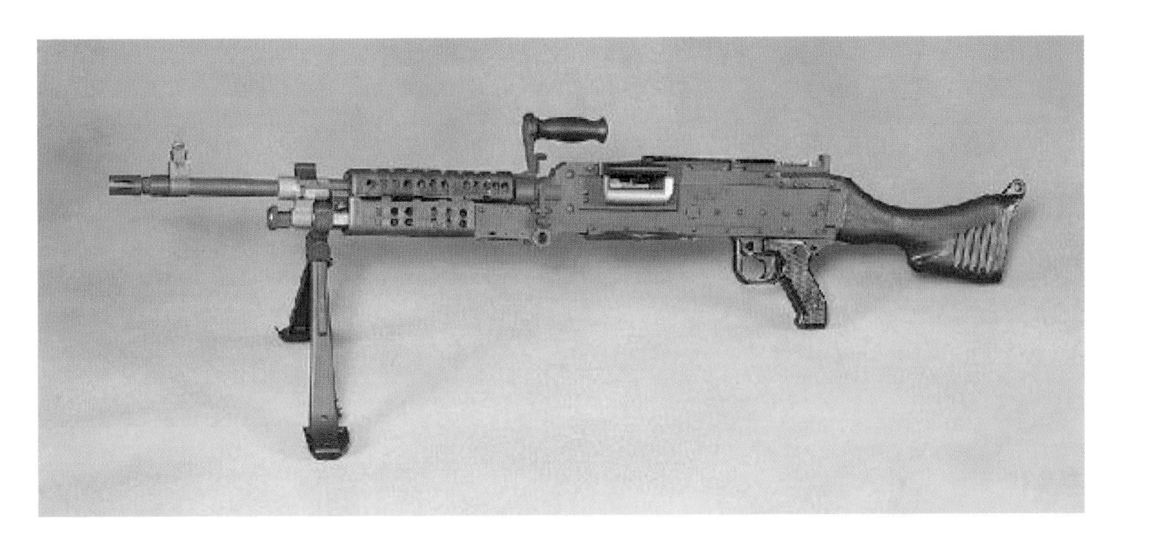

*M240 A-1*

## M249 SAW

The M249 SAW, or squad automatic weapon, is the FN Minimi, modified to meet the US Army's requirements for a light machine gun. It was approved in 1982 but did not enter production until the early 1990s due to along drawn-out period of testing and modification before the requirements were satisfied. The changes were largely to suit US manufacturing methods and were relatively small, though nonetheless important. The main exterior difference are the shape of the fore-end and butt, and the presence of a heat shield above the barrel. All other characteristics of the Minimi are unchanged.

CARTRIDGE 5.56 x 45mm NATO

DIMENSIONS
Length: 1040mm (40.95in) Weight: 6.85kg (15lb 2oz) Barrel: 523mm (20.60in) Rifling: 6 grooves, rh
Feed system: 30-round detachable box or 200-round metal belt
Cyclic rate: 750 rds/min

IN PRODUCTION 1992-

*M4 PG*

## M4 Carbine

The M4 is a true carbine, being a short-barrelled version of the M16A2 rifle fitted with a collapsible stock, and it bridges the gap between the full sized rifle and the ultra-short Commando version. Designed to provide heavyweight fire power for soldiers working in close quarters and confined spaces, it is mainly used by special forces and armoured troops. A combined safety-catch and fire selector is located on the left side of the receiver above the trigger. With the catch pulled back so that the pointer is directed to 'safe' the weapon is safe. With the catch pressed down and forward to the vertical, the weapon fires single shots. With the catch pressed forward so that the pointer is to the rear against 'auto' automatic fire is available. Over 80% of its parts and all mechanical components are interchangeable with those of the M16A2, and it will accept any NATO or STANAG 4179 magazines. As well as being used by US forces it is in service with the Canadian Army as the C8 rifle and with a number of Central and South American forces.

CARTRIDGE 5.56 x 45mm NATO

DIMENSIONS
Length, stock extended: 840mm (3307in)
Length, stock folded: 760mm (2992in)
Weight: 2.54kg (5lb 10oz) Barrel: 368mm (14.5in) Rifling: 6 grooves, rh Magazine capacity: 20 or 30 rounds
Rate of fire: 700 - 1000 rds/min

IN PRODUCTION 1984-

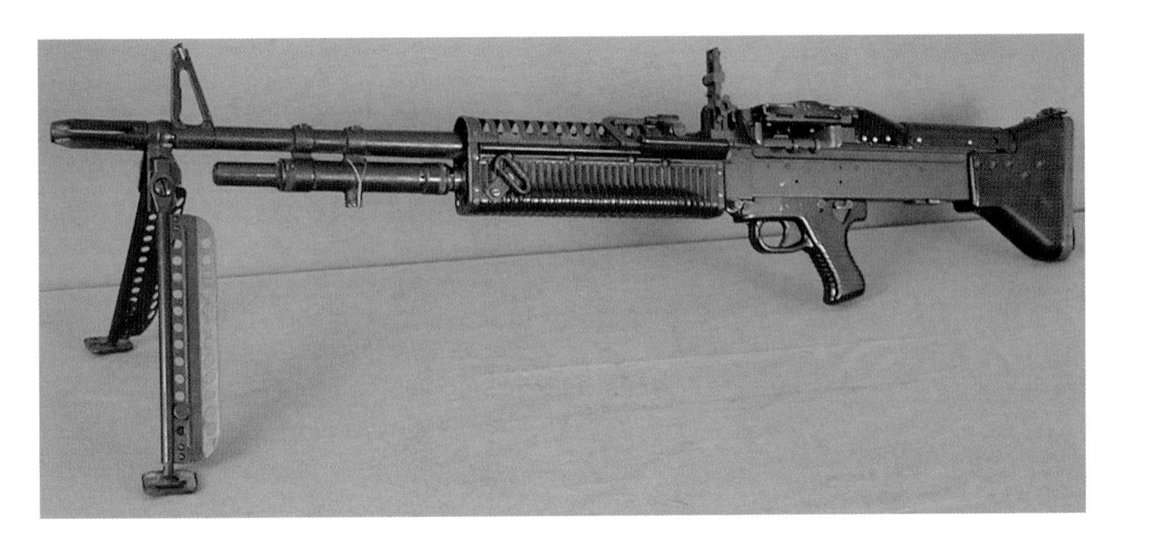



## M60, M60E1

The M60, with its modified successor the M60E1, is the standard squad general purpose machine-gun of the United States Army. It was designed in 1944 as the T44, entered production as the M60 and has been in service with US forces since the early 1960s. The M60 design used the feed system of the German MG42 and the bolt and locking system of the FG42, but the detail design was so poor that changing a barrel involved virtually dismantling the gun. The later M60E1 corrected the most serious faults, had a simpler barrel with the gas cylinder and bipod fixed to the gun, and it also had a handle for barrel changing. There were other less important changes which brought the M60E1 more into line with current practice, and gave it improved reliability. A feature of both models was the Stellite lining to the barrels that improved the wear characteristics.

CARTRIDGE 7.62 x 51 mm NATO

DIMENSIONS
Length: 1100mm (43.5in) Weight: 10.51 kg (23lb 3oz) Barrel: 560mm (22.04in) Rifling: 4 grooves, rh
Feed system: Disintegrating link belt
Cyclic rate: 550 rds/min

IN PRODUCTION 1960 -

*M1014 LTD*

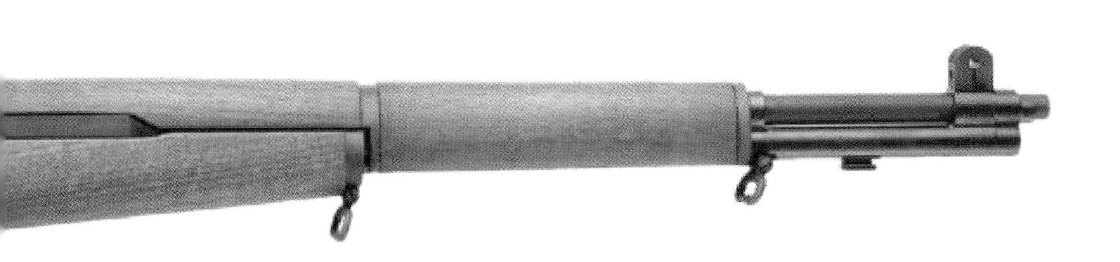

*M1 Garand*

*M1 Carbine*

*MK36 Mod 0*

*Mk48 mod 0 62mm*

*Kord 12 7mm Heavy Machine Gun*

## M60E3 AND E4

The Saco Defense Systems Division of the Maremount Corporation has long be associated with the M60 being responsible for a large part of production of the weapon. Only too well aware of its shortcomings Saco introduced the lightweight E3 and E4 models for use as squad support weapons. The M60E3 was the further development of the M60 design intended to produce a handier weapon with a forward handgrip and simplified gas and feed systems. The E4 brought a choice of three barrel and an integrated optical sight mount. The feed cover has been modified to permit it to be closed whether the bolt is forward or back, and the bipod is attached to the receiver. A winter trigger guard allows firing when wearing heavy gloves. The M60E4 was taken into use by the US Navy and Marine Corps and sold to several other countries.

CARTRIDGE 7.62 x 5lmm NATO

DIMENSIONS
Length: 1077mm (42.40in) Weight: 8.80kg (19lb 6oz) Barrel: 558mm (22.0in) Rifling: 4 grooves, rh
Feed system: disintegrating link belt
Cyclic rate: 600 rds/min

IN PRODUCTION 1994 -

## M72A1 LAW

Designed as a one-man rocket launcher for anti-tank use, the M72 has been replaced in service by the M72A1 and M72A2 (the two are identical except that the M72A2 has an increased penetration capability). When carried, the smoothbore launcher tube is closed, and in this form is waterproof. In action the end covers are opened, after removing the safety pins. The inner tube is then telescoped outwards, and this action also cocks the firing mechanism. The launcher tube is then held over the shoulder, aimed by the simple sights and fired by pressing the trigger button. The rocket motor is fully burnt by the time it leaves the launcher; one drawback is that this creates a large danger area behind the firer. Once used the launcher tube is discarded. The 66mm rocket has now become a standard infantry anti-tank weapon in many armies. The M71A1 and M71A2 are 35mm sub-calibre training devices. The model is also built in Norway by Raufoss for issue to NATO forces.

Calibre: 66 mm
Length: 89.3cm (launcher-extended)
65.5cm (launcher closed)
50.8cm (rocket)
Weight: 2.37k- (complete)
1 k- {rocket)
Muzzle velocity: 145m/s
Max effective range: 300m
Armour penetration: 30.5cm steel plate

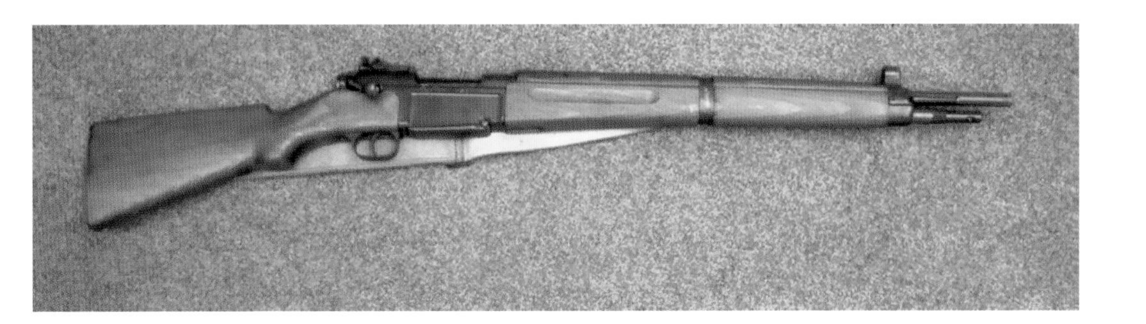



## MAS 36

The origins of the MAS 36 date back to 1924 when the introduction of a rimless 75mm cartridge, which was far better ballistically than the existing 8mm rimmed pattern, forced the French to reexamine their infantry weapons. Their service rifles, originally developed in the 1880s, were in obvious need of replacement and a development programme was put in hand.

After a series of prototypes , the B1 version of the MAS 34 was accepted for service in 1935. The production model was to be known as the MAS 36.

The MAS 36 had a distinctive shape, the pistol grip butt was separated from the fore end and hand guard by a massive slab-sided receiver containing the one piece bolt. No safety catch was provided, and the bolt was bent forward so that It came easily into the firer's hand. The back sight lay on the rear of the receiver, immediately ahead of the firer's eye. There was a single barrel band, which carried a swivel ring and a machined nose cap that mounted the front sight. The butt was fitted with a recessed strap clip. The spike type bayonet lay in a channel In the fore end and a stacking spike protruded from the right side of the nose cap.

Though the first deliveries had been made in 1937, and these rifles were used by the French army and the forces of former French colonies in Africa and the Far East, comparatively few MAS 36 rifles had reached French Infantrymen when the Germans Invaded.

The MAS 36 and its derivatives were sturdy and durable, and though the bolt was harder to operate than some of it's rivals and safety features were poor, they remained in service for many years.

Calibre 7.5mm
System of operation Turning bolt
Length 1,022mm
Weight 3.75Kg
Barrel 575mm, 4 grooves, left hand twist
Feed system 5 round internal charger loaded box magazine
Manufacturer Manufacture d'Armes de Saint-Etienne

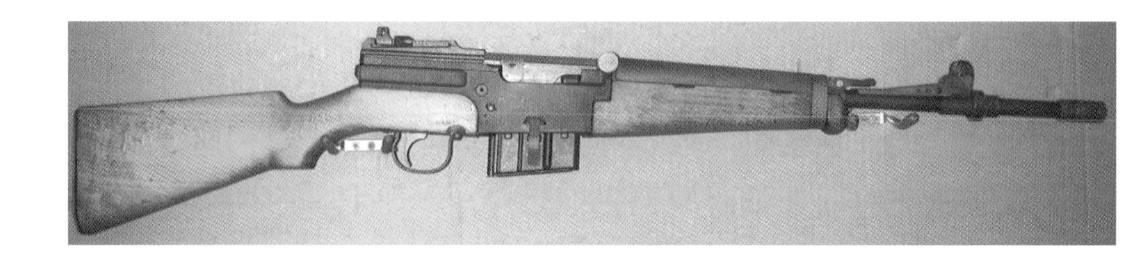



## MAS 49

After the war the French Army was in desperate need of a modern service rifle to replace the collection of pre-war weapons, acquired from various sources, with which it was equipped at the cessation of hostilities. Work had been started on a design for an automatic weapon as early as 1924 but all development was halted by the German invasion of 1939. In 1944, with the liberation of France, work was once again resumed and culminated in the MAS 49 that was issued to the troops in 1949.It bore a strong family resemblance to the MAS36 especially in its two part stock and slab-sided receiver. The new weapon, however was a semi-automatic. Gas-operated, it used direct gas blast to blow the bolt carrier backwards, instead of the more usual piston. 1956 saw the introduction of a slightly improved model, the MAS49/56. The modifications were made to conform more closely to NATO standards and consisted of changing the muzzle into a NATO standard grenade-launching configuration, with 22mm gas sealing rings. The fore-end was shortened to allow the grenade tail to fit over the barrel and the front sight was re-located to a ramp behind the grenade stop ring . A special grenade sight was also added

The MAS49 remained the standard French rifle until the arrival of the FAMAS in 1980, when large numbers were handed over to the former French colonies.

CARTRIDGE
75 x 54mm French Service

DIMENSIONS
Length o/a: 1100mm (43.3in) Weight: 4JOkg (10lb 6oz) Barrel: 580mm (22.83in) Rifling: 4 grooves, lh Magazine capacity: 10 rounds

IN PRODUCTION 1951-65

*MAT 49*

## MAT 49

This replaced the MAS 38 submachine gun and fires a far more practical cartridge. It is a very compact design and the magazine housing, complete with magazine, can be folded forward to lie under the barrel and make it more convenient for carrying. It was more or less replaced in the French Army by the adoption of the 5.56mm FA-MAS rifle, but is still widely used by reserve forces and by police and other paramilitary forces. It is also in use in former French colonies.

CARTRIDGE
9 x 19mm Parabellum

DIMENSIONS
Length, with butt extended: 690mm (26.0in)
Length, with butt folded: 404mm (15.9in)
Barrel: 230mm (9.05in)
Weight: 3.63kg (8lb 0oz)
Rifling: 4 grooves, lhMagazine capacity: 32-rounds Rate of Fire: 600 rds/min

IN PRODUCTION 1949

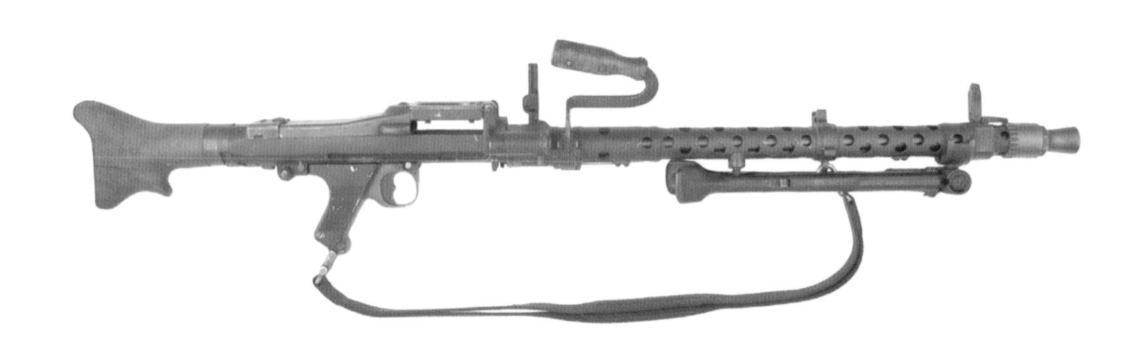

*MG34*

## MG34

The MG34 was a development of Solothurn's MG30. This was a very advanced design and about 5000 of these guns were made, most of which were bought by Austria and Hungary, and many were used during the war. The German Army decided there was room for further improvement and requested that Mauserwerke undertake additional development.

They jettisoned the side-feeding box magazine of the MG30 and made the new design a belt-fed weapon which, by quick substitution of a different feed unit, could also use the 75-round saddle drum of the MG15. Changes were also made to the action, and barrel changing was simplified.

The most far-reaching feature of the MG34 was tactical rather than mechanical; it was the first example of what is known today as the 'General Purpose' machine gun. Fitted with a bipod it functioned as the squad light automatic; on its tripodr, it functioned as a medium machine gun; and on a different pattern of light tripod, it made a good anti-aircraft weapon. It was the first belt-fed weapon to be used as a light machine gun in quantity and it proved that the concept was valid, provided the supply organisation was efficient.

Calibre 7.92mm
Length 48.0in
Weight 26lb 11oz
Barrel 24.75in long, 4 grooves, right hand twist
Feed system
Belt, or
75-round saddle drum magazine
System of operation
Recoil; revolving bolt head
Rate of fire 850rpm
Manufacturers Mauserwerke AG, Berlin Stey-Daimler-Puch AG, Austria
Waffenwerk Brunn (Brno), Czechoslovakia

*MG42*

## MG42

When the production of MG34 models was obviously insufficient for the German Army's needs, a new design of weapon was begun, one which would be easier to mass produce. For the first time the design was not left entirely in the hands of gun-makers; an expert in pressing and stamping metal, was called in to advise at an early stage in design. As a result the final design was specifically laid out to suit stamping and pressing processes, with welding and riveting used for assembly. The mechanism of the MG42 was modified from that of the MG34.

One of the results of the redesign was to raise the rate of fire to an astonishing 1200rpm, much higher than any other contemporary machine gun and a rate which has only rarely since been exceeded. As a result the barrel had to be designed for quick-changing; every 250 rounds was the recommended figure; a fresh barrel could be fitted in five seconds.

As with the MG34, the MG42 was used on a bipod as a light machine gun or on a tripod as a medium gun, though the high rate of fire made it difficult to control on a bipod. It was extremely reliable, highly resistant to dust and cold conditions and was extremely popular with the Wehrmacht. Its first use in action is said to have been by the Afrika Korps at Gazala in May 1942. Over 750,000 MG42s were made during the war, and at the war's end many countries who seized stocks of the guns adopted for use in their own armies, among them France and Yugoslavia, and when the German Bundeswehr was reconstituted and required a machine gun they simply put the MG42 back into production in 7.62mm NATO calibre as the MG1.

Calibre 7.92mm
Length 48.0in
Weight 25lb 8oz
Barrel 21.0in long, 4 grooves, right hand twist
System of operation
Recoil; roller locking
Feed system Belt
Rate of fire 1200rpm
Manufacturer Mauserwerke AG, Berlin

## Madsen

The Madsen was one of the most unusual machine guns of all time, using an action totally unlike any other, produced in virtually the same model for fifty years, used in almost every war from the Russo-Japanese to Vietnam, and yet never officially adopted in quantity by any major power. It was designed by a Dane called Schouboe, and was probably the only one of his many weapon designs which was a success. It was then adopted by the Danish cavalry and named 'Madsen', after the Danish Minister of War who had been particularly enthusiastic about its adoption. After that it was bought in small numbers by almost every nation and evaluated both in peace and war. It was the Norwegian Army's light machine gun in 1940, being used in the brief campaign against the German invasion. As well as being in use in Norway, Madsens were to be found in Estonia, Lithuania, Latvia, Poland and many other European countries, many of which found their way into German service. As well as employing them as they stood, the Germans developed an ingenious conversion unit which allowed the use of the standard German Army machine gun belts instead of the box magazines.

Calibre 7.92mm
length 45.0in
Weight 20lb
Barrel 23.0in long, 4 grooves, right hand twist
Feed system 25-, 30- or 40-round detachable box magazines
System of operation
Recoil; rising block
Rate of fire (cyclic) 450rpm
Manufacturer Dansk Rekylriffel Syndikat AS 'Madsen', Copenhagen

## Mauser SP66

The Mauser SP66 is a heavy barrelled sniping rifle. It uses the short-throw Mauser bolt action in which the handle is toward the front end of the bolt, so as to reduce the amount of movement required of the firer. It is a pure sniper rifle and incorporates various refinements not found on hunting or military weapons. The stock is adjustable in several directions, the lock time between pulling the trigger and the bullet leaving the muzzle is extremely short, and there is a combined muzzle brake and flash-hider. There is a telescope mount on the receiver that will accept a variety of optical sights including night vision devices, there are no iron sights. It is fitted with the Mauser 'Silent Safety' to prevent the sniper's position being given away by any distinctive mechanical sounds.

CARTRIDGE
7.62 x 51mm NATO
or .300 Winchester Magnum

DIMENSIONS
Length o/a: 1120mm (44.29in) Weight: 6.25kg (13lb 12oz) Barrel: 730mm (28.75in) Rifling: 4 grooves, rh Magazine capacity: 3 rounds

IN PRODUCTION 1976-

*Maxim 1910*

## Maxim 1910

The Maxim gun has had a long and distinguished career in the hands of the Russians. Hiram Maxim himself demonstrated the weapon at St. Petersburg in 1887, and eventually the Tsar's army was provided with British-made Maxims. In 1905 manufacture began at Tula Arsenal in Russia, and from then until 1945 the weapon was in more or less continuous production. The original model had a cast bronze water jacket, but in 1910 this was replaced by a steel jacket and slight improvements were made to the feed mechanism, and with that the design was frozen. The only minor changes made subsequently were the fitting of a corrugated water jacket during World War I and the fitting of a much larger filler cap, to enable the water jacket to be more easily filled with snow, during World War II.

The mechanism was, of course, the basic Maxim toggle lock operated by recoil; not the simplest mechanism ever made but certainly one of the most reliable. Where the Russian weapons were unique was in the matter of weight. The British Vickers, more or less the same gun, weighed 32.5lbs, and the German Maxim 1908, which was virtually the same gun as the Russian 1910, only 40.5lbs. Doubtless the massiveness of the Russian construction contributed to its reliability but it certainly made it a difficult proposition to move. As a result the Russians developed their unique wheeled 'Sokolov' mounting, a tubular steel trail into which the gun was mounted and which acted both as a carrying cart and a firing mounting. The wheels of the Sokolov could be removed in the winter and replaced with a pair of sledge runners, to be towed by ski-troops.

Calibre 7.62mm
Length 43.6in
Weight Gun 52lb 8oz
Mounting 110lbs
Barrel 28.4in long, 4 grooves, right hand twist
Feed system 250-round fabric belt
System of operation
Recoil; Maxim toggle lock
Rate of fire 550rpm
Manufacturer State Arsenals

## Negev

The Negev is a multi-purpose weapon that can feed from standard belts, drums or box magazines and can be fired from a bipod, tripod or vehicle mounts. The standard barrel is rifled for SS109 ammunition and there is an alternative barrel rifled to accept US M193 ammunition. The weapon is gas operated with a rotating bolt that locks into the barrel extension, and fires from an open bolt. The gas regulator has three positions, allowing the rate of fire to be changed from 650-800 rds/min to 800-950 rds/min or the gas supply can be cut off to permit launching grenades from the muzzle. The weapon will fire in semi- or full-automatic modes and, it can be used as an assault rifle by removing the bipod and attaching a normal fore-end and short barrel. The Negev was introduced in 1988 and has been adopted by the Israel Defence Force.

Cartridge 5.56 x 45mm NATO or M193

DIMENSIONS
Length, butt extended: 1020mm (40.16in)
Length, butt folded 780mm (30.71in)
Weight: unloaded 750kg (l6lb 8oz)
Barrel: 460mm (18.11in) Rifling. 6 groove, rh
Feed system. 30 or 35-round box, link belt or drum
Cyclic rate 800 rlis/min

IN PRODUCTION 1988-

## NSV

The NSV machine gun was designed by the trio of Nikitin, Volkov and Solokov, hence its name.
It first appeared in the late 1970s as a replacement weapon for the wartime DshK in Russian service. Initially introduced as a tank commander's machine gun; it was later seen on a ground mount for heavy support use by infantry, and then on an air defence mounting. The gun is gas operated, using a piston to drive a bolt carrier and can be set up during manufacture to fire from the left or from the right as required. In addition to being made in Russia, it has been licensed to Poland, Bulgaria and Yugoslavia, all of whom have offered it on the export market for some years.
There are two main variants the NSVT, adapted for use as co-axial tank armament, and the NSV-N4 fitted with night vision sights.

CARTRIDGE 12.7 x l07mm Soviet

DIMENSIONS
Length o/a: l560mm (61.4in) Weight: 25.00k,1 (55lb 2oz) Barrel: I070mm (42.12in) Rifling 8 grooves: rh Feed system: belt
Rate of fire 700 rds/min

IN PRODUCTION 1971

## PGM Hegate

The 12.7mm PGM Hegate is an anti-material sniping rifle produced by PGM Precision, the well-known rifle makers. In the late 1980s they developed a range of sniping rifles, widely adopted by French and other continental police forces. The 'Hecate' is essentially a scaled-up version of their 'Intervention' sniping rifle and is a conventional bolt-action repeating rifle. The wooden butt, together with its monopod and cheek-piece, can be removed for transportation. There is a bipod attached to the receiver fore-end, and a pistol grip. A large single-baffle muzzle brake reduces the recoil to a reasonable amount, and this can be removed and replaced by a silencer. The rifle has been taken into use by the French Army and is now marketed in Belgium by FN HERSTAL.

CARTRIDGE
.50 Browning

DIMENSIONS
Length o/a: 1380mm (54.33in)
Weight: 13.5kg (29lb 12oz)
Barrel: 700mm (27.56in)
Rifling: 8 grooves, rh
Magazine capacity: 7 rounds

IN PRODUCTION 1988-

SAFETY
Manual safety catch on right side of receiver, locks sear and trigger.

## PIAT

The Projector, Infantry, Anti-Tank (or PIAT, by which name it inevitably became known) was the result of several years of trial and experiment by Lt-Col Blacker, RA, who desginged the launcher and Major Jeffris, who developed the holow charge warhead. Lt-Col Blacker had long been attracted by the idea of a spigot discharger; such a device dispenses with the usual barrel and replaces it with a hollow tail unit on the projectile. A percussion cartridge within this tail unit is struck by a firing spigot, a heavy steel rod which is driven into the tail while the projectile is supported on a simple tray. The explosion of the cartridge blows the projectile from the spigot, the length of its travel along the spigot being sufficient to impart direction. Blacker's first patent for this type of weapon appeared in the early 1930s but it was to be August 1942, after a great deal of development, before final approval was given.
The mechanism of the PIAT was very simple; an enormous spring was compressed by unlatching the shoulder pad, standing on it, and lifting the weapon so that the spring and spigot were withdrawn into the body and held by a simple sear mechanism. The body was then returned to the shoulder pad and the weapon was ready to fire. A bomb was placed in guideways at the front and on pressing the trigger the spigot was released, entering the tail unit of the bomb and exploding the propelling cartridge. This explosion blew the bomb off, and at the same time blew the spigot back into the body of the weapon, recocking it ready for the next shot. The maximum engagement range was about 100 yards, although the bomb could reach to 750 yards.

Calibre Not applicable
Length 39in
Weight 32lb
Barrel None
Feed system Single shot
System of operation Spigot discharger
Muzzle velocity ca 350ft/sec
Penetration ca 75mm
Projectile & weight Hollow charge, 3lb

*PK mg Russia*

## PK mg Russia

The PK was the first general purpose machine gun to go into Soviet service; it replaced the RP46 but, surprisingly, retained the old rimmed cartridge, presumably because of its better long-range performance when compared to the M1943 rimless round. The design is a combination of Kalashnikov breech mechanism and a new feed system; it is light in weight and well made. There are a number of variant models the PK is the basic company gun; the PKS is the tripod-mounted weapon; the PKT is the version for use in tanks with no pistol grip or butt. As with other Soviet designs, the PK family saw service with all of the former Warsaw Pact countries.

CARTRIDGE
7.62 x 54R Soviet

DIMENSIONS
Length o/a: 1193mm (47.0in)
Weight: 890kh (191b 10oz)
Barrel: 660mm (26.0in)
Rifling: 4 grooves, rh
Feed system: belt
Rate of fire: 650 rds/min

IN PRODUCTION 1964

## PTRD 1941

Design of the 14.5mm PTRD 1941 started in 1932 when it was decided to replace the 12.8mm anti-tank rifle then in service. For the new weapon, a completely new cartridge of 14.5mm calibre, one of the heaviest ever developed, was produced.

The weapon, designed by Degtyarev, looks extremely simple, even agricultural, but it conceals one or two refinements beneath its rough exterior. The barrel recoils within a slide so that the recoil carries the bolt handle against a cam and lifts it to unlock the breech; the bolt is then held while the barrel moves back to its firing position, during which movement the empty case is extracted and ejected. The firer then inserts a fresh cartridge and closes the bolt by hand.

The bullet fired by the PTRD was originally a steel-cored streamlined type carrying a small charge of incendiary composition in the nose which gave a flash on impact to indicate the point of strike. But streamlined bullets are only of value in long range weapons, and in 1941 a new design of square based bullet with a tungsten carbide core was introduced. This improved velocity and penetration at the short ranges. The rifle appears to have remained in service throughout the war.

Calibre 14.5mm
Length 79in
Weight 38lb
Barrel 48.3in long, 8 grooves, right hand twist
Feed system Single shot
System of operation Bolt action
Muzzle velocity 3300ft/sec
Penetration 25mm/500m/0 degrees
Manufacturer State Arsenals

## PTRS 1941

The PTRS rifle was developed at the same time as the PTRD by the well-known designer Simonov, and the mechanism exhibits many similarities with his better known automatic rifle designs. It was a very advanced weapon, using a top-mounted gas cylinder and piston to operate a bolt carrier. This cammed the bolt down to unlock it, then moved it back to extract and eject in the usual loading cycle. The magazine, front-hinged for cleaning like other Simonov designs, took 5 rounds loaded with a special clip that could only be loaded one way; sometimes inconvenient in the heat of in battle.

Although a more advanced design than the PTRD, the PTRS was much less robust in use as well as being heavier and larger. Although retained in service until the late 1940s it is believed that relatively few were manufactured, the PTRD having the same performance, since it used the same ammunition, and being easier to use and produce. It is thought that both models were accepted for service as an insurance policy in case either should turn out to be unsuccessful, and that once the PTRD had demonstrated its reliability, production of the PTRS was either closed down or converted to the PTRD.

Calibre 14.5mm
Length 84in
Weight 46lb
Barrel 48in long, 8 grooves, right hand twist
Feed system 5-round box magazine
System of operation Gas; semi-automatic; tipping bolt
Muzzle velocity 3320ft / sec
Penetration 25mm/ 500m/ 0 degrees
Manufacturer State Arsenals

## PANZERBUCHSE 38

The German PzB 38 anti-tank rifle was an elegant design with a very good performance obtained by using a 7.92mm bullet married to a 13mm cartridge so as to give an extremely powerful propelling charge. The mechanism was unusual in that the breech closure was by a vertical sliding block on the lines of an artillery weapon. To operate the weapon the breech was opened by swinging the pistol grip forward and down, whereupon the block was held open by the extractors and the pistol grip could be returned to its normal place. A cartridge was then loaded by hand, releasing the extractors and allowing the breech block to close by spring pressure. On firing, the weapon recoiled in its stock and a cam opened the block to eject the empty case on the return movement of the barrel, coming to rest with the block held open ready for the next round to be loaded.

The PzB 38 seems to have been little used in combat. The only likely theatre for its use would have been the Polish campaign, since it was largely replaced in service by the PzB 39 before the 1940 campaign in France. In any event the rapid movements of the attacking German Army did not offer much opportunity for the use of anti-tank rifles.

Calibre 7.92mm
Length 51in
Weight 35lb
Barrel 43in long, 4 grooves, right hand twist
Feed system Single shot
System of operation Vertical sliding block, semi-automatic
Muzzle velocity 3975ft/sec
Penetration 25mm/300m/30 degrees
Manufacturer Rheinmettal-Borsig AG, Dusseldorf

## PANZERBUCHSE 39

The Panzerbuchse 39 was essentially a simplified PzB 38 intended to be better suited to manufacture in quantity. The vertical sliding breech-block was retained but the semi-automatic action was discarded, the block being entirely hand operated by swinging the pistol grip back and forth. The recoiling barrel was also dropped, but a muzzle brake was added, so that the recoil felt by the firer was about the same as before. A minor addition was the fitting of two ready-use magazines, small boxes each containing ten rounds clipped to brackets at each side of the breech where they could be reached easily by the firer. This was an idea that dated back to the 'quick-loader' which was common on Continental single-shot military rifles in the 1880s.

Since the barrel was almost the same length and the ammunition was the same, the performance of the PzB 39 was equal to that of the PzB 38. But apart from very limited use in the 1940 campaign in France, the PzB saw very little action.

Caliber 7.92mm
Length 62.25in
Weight 27.251b
Barrel 42.75in long, 4 grooves, right hand twist
Feed system Single shot
System of operation Vertical sliding block, hand operated
Muzzle velocity 3975ft/sec
Penetration 25mm/300m/30 degrees
Manufacturers Rheinmettal-Borsig, Dusseldorf
Steyr-Daimler-Puch AG, Vienna

## Panzerfaust

In 1942 the appearance of a new generation of Russian tanks led to a demand for a light but potent anti-tank weapon for infantry use, and a Dr. Langweiler of the Hugo Schneider Aktien Gesellschaft (HASAG) was given the task of developing a suitable weapon during the summer of that year .

After a period of develoment and production of several prototypes Langweiler arrived at the design of what was to be known as the Panzerfaust 30. This recoilless device consisted of a tube carrying a small gunpowder charge in its centre and with a hollow charge bomb in one end. A trigger fired the gunpowder charge, this launched the bomb forward, while the rearward blast from the other end of the tube balanced the recoil. The tube was extended in length so that the flash was directed behind the holder, and a simple sight was fitted,. The bomb was given thin spring steel fins which wrapped around the tail shaft while the bomb lay in the tube and the warhead was of much greater diameter than the tube. The name Panzerfaust 30, indicated the fighting range in meters. After a variety of tests it was put into production in October 1943 at a rate of 200,000 per month. Another version, the Panzerfaust 30 Klein, using a small diameter bomb, was also put into production, its target production being 100,000 per month.

Subsequent versions were modified to provide increasingly greater ranges.

Tube 31.5in
Bomb Length 14.25in
Diameter, bomb 3.95in
Velocity ft/sec 98
Penetration at 11° 140mm
Weight complete 7.5lb

## Panzerschreck

The 8.8cm Raketen Panzerbuchse 54 or Panzerschreck (Tank Terror) was a shoulder fired rocket launcher inspired by the US Army's 2.36in Bazooka after specimens had been captured by the Germans. At that time the German Army were casting about for a suitable weapon to use against Soviet tanks, and after trials of the Bazooka it was decided to produce a German equivalent as quickly as possible.

The opportunity was taken of making a few improvements in the original American design that were later incorporated by the Americans in later models of their weapon. The calibre was increased to 88mm in order to provide a better and more effective warhead; a drum tail was used, and the electric firing current was derived from an impulse magneto driven by squeezing the firing gap. As with most of the first-generation launchers, the rocket motor was still burning when it left the launcher and therefore a shield, which incorporated the rear sight, was provided. The weapon became notorious for the flame and smoke which came from the rear end when it was fired, a characteristic which gave rise to the nickname 'Ofenrohr' (Stovepipe).

The Panzerschreck was widely used, being first issued in 1943 to units on the Eastern Front and remaining on issue throughout the war. As the propellant situation became more critical, other weapons were developed to replace it, but few reached the hands of troops, so in spite of this logistic drawback it stayed in use. It was highly effective against the tanks of the time, and appears to have been well liked by the soldiers who used it.

Calibre 88.9mm
Length 64.5in Weight 20.25lb
Barrel 62.5in long, smoothbore
System of operation Single shot rocket launcher
Projectile & weight Hollow charge, 7.25lb
effective Range 150m
Penetration ca 100mm at 0 degrees

*RPD*

## Pecheneg mg Russia

This is the latest incarnation of the PK series of machine guns that first saw service in 1964.

The Pecheneg, has an 80% commonality of parts with the earlier weapon but introduces a new, fixed barrel with a forced-draught cooling system allowing the gun to fire, approximately 1,000 rounds per hour or 600 rounds in 40 to 50-round bursts.

The PK weapons must rank among the most numerous of all modern machine-guns, being used

not only by the Soviet and Warsaw Pact armies and their successors, but also by a large number of export customers including the Chinese, who use the type in the form of their Type 80 copy made-in China.

Calibre: 7.62-mm (0.3-in)
Length overall: 1160 mm (45.7 in)
Length of barrel: 658 mm (25.9 in)
Weights:
Gun empty: 9kg (19.84 lb)
Tripod 7.5 kg (16.53 lb);
100-round belt 2.44 kg (5.38 lb)
Muzzle velocity: 825 m (2,707 ft) per second
Rate of fire, cyclic: 690- 720 rpm
Feed: 100-, 200- and 250-round metal-link belts

## RPD

The RPD was for some years the standard light machine-gun of the Soviet Army, having been introduced in the 1950s as the complementary squad weapon to the AK rifle. It was the logical development of the earlier DP and DPM, and it was progressively improved during its life. It was a gas operated weapon and the modifications were mainly to the gas piston system to improve stability and provide sufficient power to lift the belt under adverse conditions. The replaceable barrel of the DP was abandoned in this fresh design, and firing was limited to no more than 100 rounds a minute to prevent overheating the barrel. The remainder of the mechanism was similar to the DP, suitably scaled down for the smaller ammunition, and, like its predecessor the DP, the RPD was capable of automatic fire only.

CARTRIDGE
7.62 x 39mm

DIMENSIONS
Length: 41.00in (1041mm)
Weight unloaded: 15lb 7oz (7.0kg)
Barrel 20.50in (520mm)
Rifling: 4 grooves, rh
Feed system 100 round belt
Cyclic rate 700 rds/min

IN PRODUCTION 1952

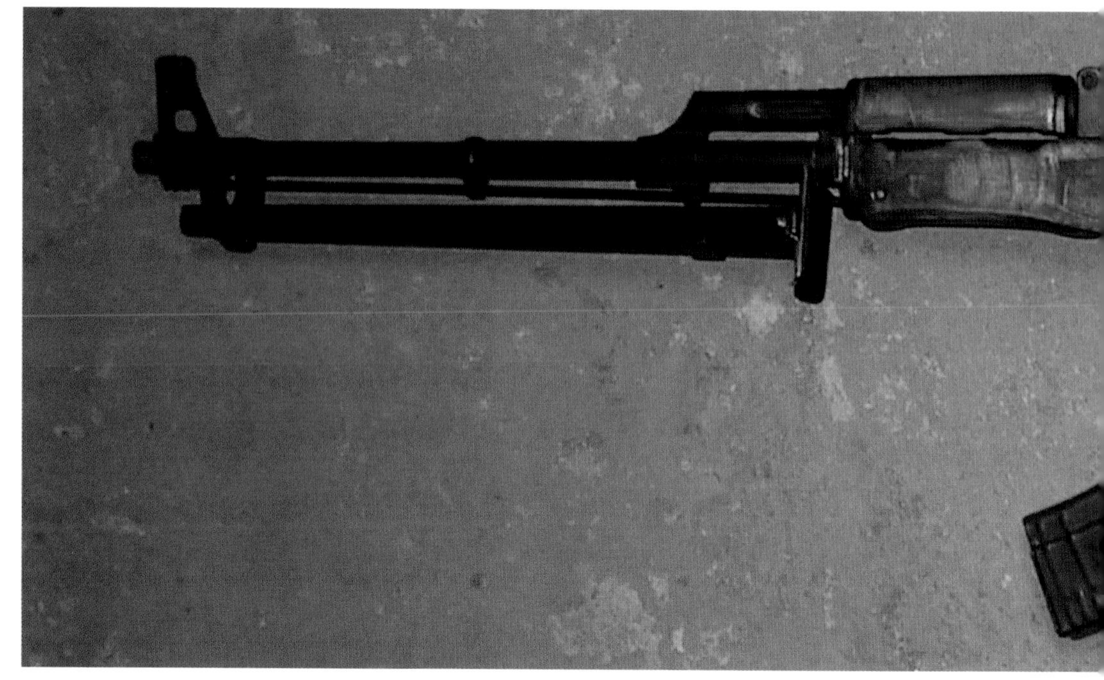

*RPK*

## RPK

The RPK was developed as the light machine gun companion weapon to the PK general-purpose machine gun. It replaced the RPD as the standard squad automatic for Soviet infantry and then went on to arm the Warsaw Pact armies and be distributed to Soviet client states across the world. It is a heavy barrelled version of the standard AK47 rif1e and it will accept AK magazines, which makes re-supply in the field relatively easy. Like the rifle, the barrel is fixed, so that sustained fire is not entirely practical, though the bore and chamber are chromium-plated in an endeavour to keep the wear rate down as far as possible.
I977 saw the introduction of a new version of the RPK. The RPK-74 bears the same relationship to the AK-74 rifle as the RPK does to the AK-47 rifle; in other words it is the heavy-barrel squad automatic in 5.45mm calibre.

CARTRIDGE
7.62 x 39mm Soviet M1943

DIMENSIONS
Length: 1035mm (40.75in)
Weight unloaded: 4.75kg (10lb 8oz)
Barrel 590mm (20.23in)
Rifling: 4 grooves, rh
Feed system: 3 or 40 round box or 75 round drum
Cyclic rate: 660 rds/min

IN PRODUCTION 1955

## RP 46

The RP46 was a development of the DPM, intended for use as a company support gun The basic layout of the DPM was retained, the principal addition being that of a belt feed so that sustained fire could be delivered. However, the original 47 round DP drum can still be used if required, so the RP46 could still be used in the squad automatic role. The barrel has been made heavier, again something demanded by the sustained fire role. It was replaced in Soviet service by the RPD, which was a further modification of the original DP design, and almost all of the RP46s were shipped to Soviet client states overseas.

CARTRIDGE
7.62 x 54R Soviet

DIMENSIONS
Length o/a: 1283mm (50.5in)
Weight. 1300kg (28lb 11oz)
Barrel: 607mm (23.9in)
Rifling: 4 grooves, rh
Feed system: 250-round cloth belt
Rate of fire: 600 rds/min

IN PRODUCTION: 1946-54

## RPG7-V

The RPG 7V was the standard rifle-squad antitank weapon of the Warsaw Pact Forces and was a recoilless, shoulder fired, muzzle loaded re-loadable weapon. It fires a PG- 7V HEAT rocket, 9.25cm in diameter and weighing 2.2kg with a muzzle velocity as it leaves the barrel of 100m/s. Within 10m a rocket motor fires and this boosts its velocity to 300m/s. The warhead weighs 1.75kg and will penetrate 32cm of armour. It has a piezo-electric fuse incorporating a self-destruct device that operates when the round is approx 900m from the launcher. There is also a training round called the PUS- 7.

This weapon is recognisable by its two handgrips with the trigger on the foremost grip, optical sight on the left hand side of the weapon and the funnel shaped venturi at the rear. The RPG- 7V was fitted with a PGO-7 or PGO-7V optical sight that is marked from 200m to 500m at steps of l00m. The sight has a x25 magnification and a 13° field of view. Open sights are provided for emergency use. If required this weapon can be fitted with the NSP-2 infrared night sighting device.

The RPG 7D is a special model for the use of the airborne forces and can be quickly broken down into two components.

The RPG 7V is built in China under the designation of Type 69 Anti-Tank Grenade Launcher.

Calibre: 85mm (launcher), 40mm (tube)
Weight of launcher: 6.3kg (including telescopic sight)
Length of tube: 95cm
Range: 500m (stationary target), 300m (moving target!
Rate of fire: 4-6rpm
Crew: 2

## Redeye FIM 43A

The first operational infantry SAM in the world, Redeye entered US Army service in 1964 and some 100,000 were delivered to the US Army and Marine Corps. It has severe limitations; there is no IFF, engagement depends on correct identification by the operator of the nature of the target aircraft. The infrared homer can only lock onto the tailpipes of an aircraft so the operator can only fire on departing aircraft after an attack. Flight speed is only just enough to catch a modern attack aircraft and the guidance is vulnerable to IRCM (Infrared Counter Measures). Once the aircraft has passed the operator must aim on a pursuit course, listen for the IR lock-on buzzer, fire the missile, and then select a fresh tube. The seeker cell needs a cooling unit, three of which are packed with each missile tube.

Type: Shoulder-fired infantry surface-to-air missile.
Dimensions: Length 48in (122cm); body diameter 2.75in (7cm); span 5.5in (14cm).
Launch weight: 18lb (8.2kg); whole package 29lb (13kg).
Propulsion: Atlantic Research dual-thrust solid fuel rocket motor.
Guidance: Initial optical aiming, infra-red homing.
Range: Up to about 2 miles (3.3km).
Flight speed: Mach 2.5.
Warhead: Smooth-case fragmentation

## Remington M40A1 Sniper

Currently in service with the US Marine Corps, the Remington M40A1 Sniper is a militarised version of the commercial Remington 700 sporting rifle. It is a bolt action repeating rifle with a bolt of Remington design, using two lugs locking into the receiver behind the chamber. There is a catch inset into the front of the trigger guard which, when pressed, allows the bolt to be removed from the receiver. The butt stock is made of wood and the barrel is particularly heavy and rigid. No iron sights are fitted, as the rifle is issued with a 10x telescope sight.

CARTRIDGE
7.62 x 51mm NATO

DIMENSIONS
Length o/a- 1118mm (44.0in)
Weight: 6.57kg (14lb 8oz)
Barrel- 610mm (24.0in)
Rifling: 4 grooves, rh
Magazine capacity: 5 rounds

IN PRODUCTION 1965-

## Rifle No.5 Mk 1 Jungle Carbine

The Rifle No 5 Mk I was designed in response to the need for a weapon more suited than the standard weapon to the jungle fighting in which British troops were involved in Burma and the Far East. The No1 and No4 Lee-Enfield rifles were too long and awkward for use in heavily overgrown terrain and it was decided to produce a shortened version of the No4.

The new design included a shorter barrel and fore stock, and sights modified to suit the changed ballistics of the weapon. The Jungle Carbine was also provided with a flash hider and a rubber pad on the butt, both intended to offset the effects of firing a normal rifle bullet from a short barrel, namely the large muzzle flash and ferocious recoil.

The new weapon was never very popular in service, but it was much handier in a jungle environment, and over 100,000 were produced.

Calibre: 0303 in (7.7mm)
Length overall: 1003 mm (39.5 in)
Length of barrel: 476 mm (18.75 in)
Weight 31.5 kg (7.15lb)
Muzzle velocity: about 730 m (2,400 ft) per second
Magazine: 10 round box

*SIG SG540 series*

## 82-PM 41 MORTAR

The army of the USSR, controlled the development of a large number of mortar types over the years, and the surprising thing is that many of them, dating from before World War II remain in large scale service. These mortars are of the light, medium and heavy types in standard calibres, although it was the heavy mortar type, starting with a calibre of 107mm (4.22in), on which they later concentrated, the Soviets did make use of medium mortars. The first of these was the 82-PM 36, which was introduced in 1936 as a copy of a Brandt muzzle loaded and smooth bore weapon The following 82-PM 37 differed mainly in its use of a round rather than square base-plate, and in the introduction of recoil springs between the barrel and the bipod. The 82-PM 41 was intended to improve the basic weapon's mobility, and instead of the bipod had a stub axle arrangement with two pressed steel wheels and, in its centre, the elevating rod.

Calibre: 82mm (3.13in)
Length: barrel 112 0mmm (48.03 in)
Weight: mortar 52 kg (114.6 lb)
Maximum range: 2550m (2790yds)

## SIG SG540 SERIES

The SIG SG540 series was designed by SIG of Switzerland and was licensed to Manurhin of France for manufacture in 1977. This arrangement circumvented Swiss arms export laws that made it impossible for SIG to supply weapons to most countries. Manurhin made about 20,000 for the French Army who used them while FAMAS rifle production got up to speed, and they were also supplied to Chile, Bolivia, Paraguay, Ecuador and Nicaragua. In 1988 the license was relinquished and passed to INDEP of Portugal who reassigned it to FAMAE of Chile, who currently make the 540 and 542. The SIG SG540 family runs to three models

CARTRIDGE
5.56 x 45mm or 7.62 x 51 mm

DIMENSIONS: (SG542)
Length o/a: 1000mm (39.37in)
Weight: 355kg (71b 13oz)
Barrel: 465mm (18.31 in)
Rifling. 4 grooves, rh
Magazine capacity: 20 or 30 rounds
Rate of fire: 800 rds/min

IN PRODUCTION 1977-

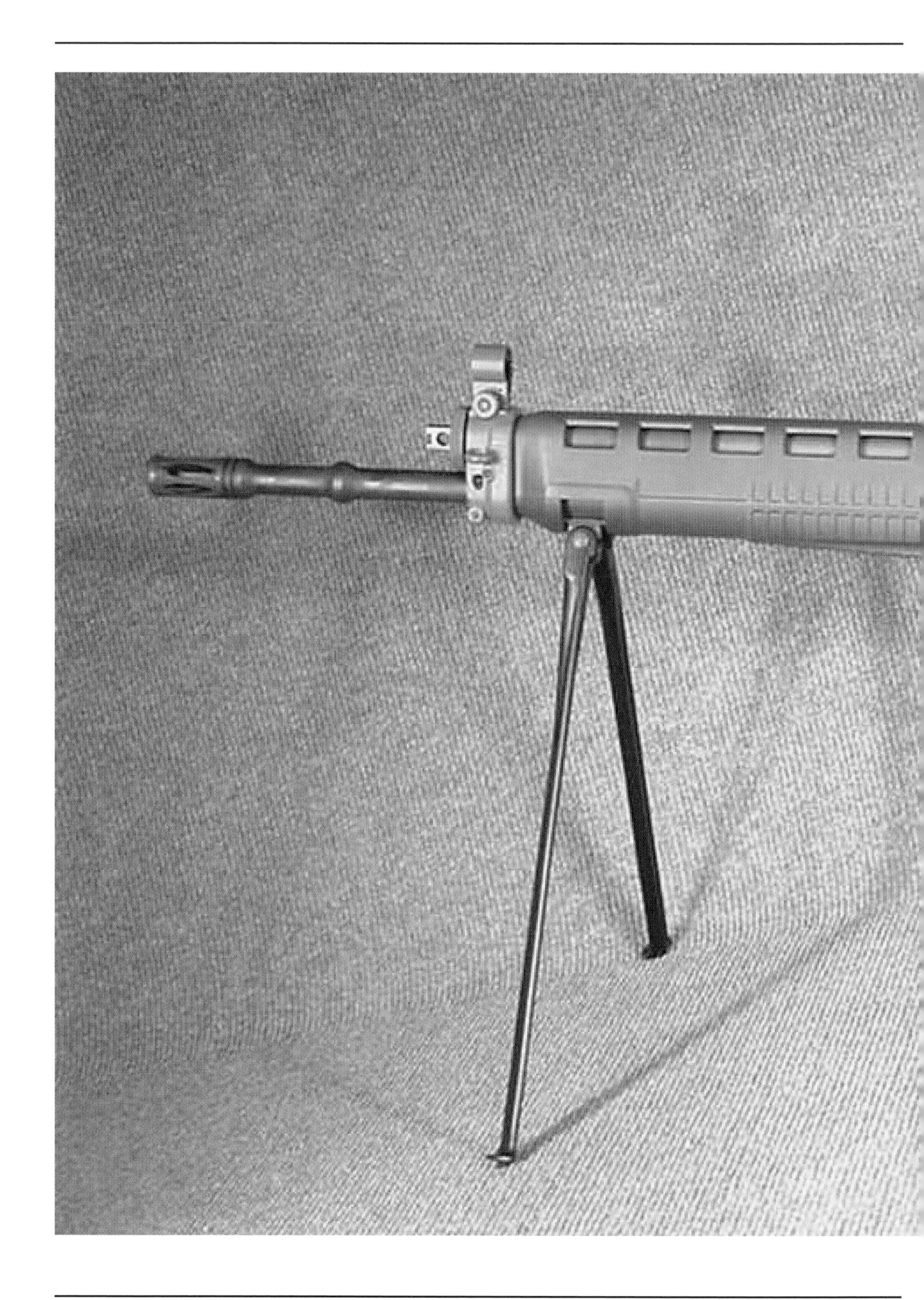

*SIG SG550*

## SIG SG550 (Stgw90)

The SIG SG550 is a development of the SG540 produced to meet a Swiss Army requirement in 1984. The SIG weapon was selected from several competing designs and became the Sturmgewehr 90, the successor to the Stgw 57 as the official Swiss army rifle. It is also made in a civilian version, without automatic fire. In comparison to the SG540 thr Stgw 90 makes greater use of synthetic materials and has a translucent plastic magazine with studs and slots to enable two or three magazines to be clipped together side-by-side. One can then be inserted into the magazine housing, and when the last shot is fired, changing to a full magazine can be done by pulling the assembly out, shifting it sideways and pushing in one of the loaded magazines.

CARTRIDGE
5.56 x 45mm NATO

DIMENSIONS: (SG552)
Length stock extended: 998mm (39.30in)
Length stock folded: 772mm (30.40in)
Weight: 4.10kg (9lb 1oz)
Barrel: 528mm (20.79in)
Rifling. 6 grooves, rh
Magazine capacity: 20 or 30 rounds
Rate of fire: 700 rds/min

IN PRODUCTION 1986-

## SIG SSG550 Sniper

The SSG550 is the sniper derivative of the standard SG550 rifle. It is fitted with a heavy hammer-forged barrel and the mechanism has been altered to provide semi-automatic fire only. There are no iron sights and no muzzle attachments. The trigger is a two-stage type, adjustable to the firer's personal preference, and the butt is adjustable for length and has an adjustable cheek-piece. The pistol grip is also adjustable for rake and carries a hand-rest that can be positioned as required. A two-position safety catch is located on the right and left sides of the receiver, above the pistol grip. A bipod is fitted, and the telescopes position can be altered to the firer's preference. An anti-reflective screen can be drawn up over the top of the rifle, which also prevents air disturbance due to barrel heat interfering with the sight line.

CARTRIDGE
5.56 x 45mm

DIMENSIONS
Length butt extended: 1130mm (44.49in)
Length, butt folded: 905mm (35.63in)
Barrel: 650mm (25.60in)
Weight. 7.3kg (16lb 1oz)
Rifling: 6 grooves, rh
Magazine capacity: 20 or 30 rounds

IN PRODUCTION

## SIG Sauer SSG 3000

The SIG Sauer SSG 3000 is a military and police sniping rifle derived from the successful Sauer 200STR target rifle. It uses the 200STRs non-rotating bolt mechanism, that uses hinged lugs to lock the bolt into the receiver when the bolt handle is turned down. It is modular in construction, screw clamps join the barrel and receiver, and the trigger and magazine systems form a single unit that slots into the receiver. The stock is of laminated wood and the fore-end is ventilated to counter possible heat warping of the heavy barrel. There is a rail under the fore-end to take a bipod or a firing sling. There are no iron sights; a mount for the standard Hensoldt telescope sight is normal, but a NATO STANAG sight mount can also be fitted.

CARTRIDGE
7.62 x 51mm NATO

DIMENSIONS
Length o/a: 1180mm (45.45in)
Weight: 5.40kg (11lb 14oz)
Barrel: 610mm (24.06in)
Rifling: 4 grooves, rh
Magazine capacity: 5 rounds

IN PRODUCTION 1991

## Sako M90

Sako originated as a government factory in the 1920s and merged with Valmet in 1987. The Sako M90 is the successor to the Valmet M62/M76 series of Finnish service rifles,. Essentially an improved Kalashnikov, the M90 uses the Kalashnikov gas operated rotating bolt action but refined and lightened. There is no wood, the fore-end and pistol grip both being steel with a plastic coating; the butt is a large-diameter tube with a cross-member welded on at the end, and there is a prominent combined flash-hider and grenade-launcher. In comparison to the Kalashnikov the M90 also has a new side-folding butt, and new sights with night-firing aids. It is now in service with the Finnish armed forces.

CARTRIDGE
7.62mm x 39mm Soviet M1943
or 5.56mm x 45 NATO

DIMENSIONS 7.62mm version
Length stock extended: 930mm (36.6in)
Length stock folded: 675mm (26.58in)
Weight: 3.85kg (8lb 8oz)
Barrel: 480mm (18.9in)
Rifling: 4 grooves, rh
Magazine capacity: 30 rounds
Rate of fire: 700 rds/min

IN PRODUCTION 1991-

*Sako TRG*

## Sako TRG

The TRG is a specialised sniping rifle. It is a bolt-action repeater, half-stocked with no hand guard and a deeply curved pistol-grip butt with a cheek-piece. The receiver and the heavy barrel are both made of cold forged steel, and there is a combined flash hider and muzzle brake that can be removed and replaced with a silencer. The action and barrel are mounted to an aluminium skeleton frame, to which is attached the synthetic stock and fore-end. The stock is fully adjustable in every direction and is also capable of adaptation to right or left-handed firers. The TRG21 is the 7.62mm model; and the TRG41 fires .08 Lapua Magnu; it has a 690mm barrel and a 5 round magazine.

CARTRIDGE
7.62 x 51mm NATO
or .308 Lapua Magnum

DIMENSIONS
Length o/a: 1150mm (45.27in)
Weight: 4.70kg (10lb 6oz)
Barrel: 660mm (26.0in)
Rifling: 4 grooves, rh
Magazine capacity: 10 rounds

IN PRODUCTION 1992-

SAFETY
Manual safety catch inside the trigger guard. Press forward to fire, pull back to make safe. This locks the bolt, trigger and firing pin.

## SCHWERE 12CM GRANATWERFER 42

In the early days of their advance against Russia in 1941, the German Army captured vast quantities of artillery material, amongst which were large numbers of the 12cm Soviet Mortar Model 1938. In Soviet hands this was an artillery weapon, but the German Army issued it as an infantry mortar under the nomenclature GrW 378(r). It was successful and well-liked by its new operators, and as a result it was decided to manufacture a German copy, which was issued late in 1942 as the GrW 42. There were some small differences in the German design, both to improve the weapon and to facilitate manufacture by German methods.

The design of the mortar was quite conventional. A smooth-bore barrel was locked into a circular base plate and supported by a bipod with a two-spring shock absorber unit connecting the barrel and bipod together. For movement, a transporter was provided; this was a frame-work of steel tubing carrying two short axles on which were mounted pressed-steel wheels on the German model (wire spoked on the Russian) with pneumatic tires. A towing eye at the front end allowed it to be pulled by any convenient vehicle. At the front end of the framework was a circular clamp to hold the mortar barrel, and the rear end was formed into a U-shape which fitted into two brackets on the base plate of the mortar .

Calibre 120mm
Barrel 73.5in long, smoothbore
Weight
Barrel 231lb
Bipod 154lb
Base plate 243lb
In action 628lb
In Transit 1234lb
Firing mechanism Selective drop or trip
Elevation 45-84 degrees
Traverse 8 to 16 degrees, varying with elevation
Projectile & weight HE 34.83lb
Maximum range 6615yds
Rate of fire 15rpm

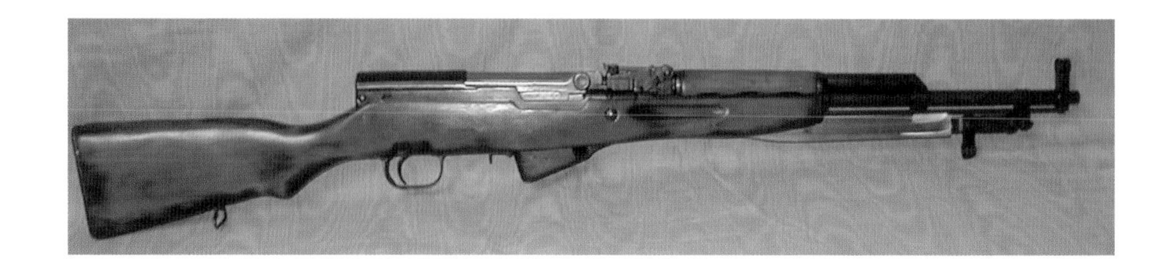

*Siminov SKS*

## Siminov SKS

Designed by Sergei Gavrilovich Simonov creator of the prewar M1936 AVS automatic, the SKS was a further development of the improved SVS, which was itself developed from the AVS. The AVS was rejected in favour of the Tokarev SVT in comparative trials but undeterred Simonov persevered with his development until the German invasion took place in 1941. He returned to it when the Soviets captured their first MP44s from the Germans and developed their own short 7.62mm cartridge. Changing the design to suit the new cartridge, experimental models were in the hands of the troops in combat in 1944, modifications were made, and in 1946 mass-production of the first Soviet weapon to fire the 7.62 x 39mm cartridge began. It was went on to be widely issued, and was also supplied to several Communist bloc countries, and was copied in China, North Korea, East Germany and Yugoslavia It is estimated that about 15 million have been made.

CARTRIDGE
7.62mm x 39mm Soviet M1943

DIMENSIONS
Length o/a: 1122mm (44.17in)
Weight: 3.86kg (8lb 8oz)
Barrel: 620mm (24.4in)
Rifling: 4 grooves, rh
Magazine capacity: 10 rounds

IN PRODUCTION 1946-

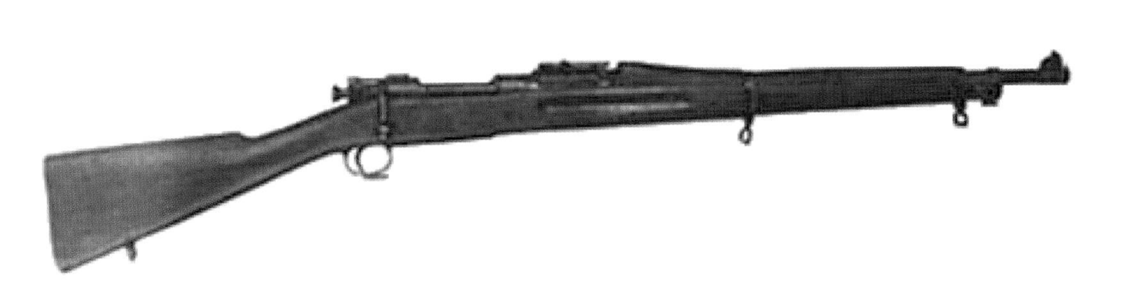

*Springfiel 1903*

## Star Z 84

The Z-84 replaced the earlier Z-70B in Spanish service in the middle 1980s and is a thoroughly modern and compact design using pressed metal for lightness and ease of production. The centre of balance is above the pistol grip, so that it can easily be fired one-handed if necessary. As well as being used by Spain, numbers have been sold to security forces in several countries.

CARTRIDGE
9mm Parabellum

DIMENSIONS
Length: stock extended: 615mm (24.2in)
Length, stock retracted: 410mm(16.14in)
Barrel: 215mm (8.46in)
Weight, empty: 3.0kg (61b 10oz)
Rifling: 6 grooves, rh
Magazine capacity: 25 or 30 rounds
Rate of fire: 600 rds/min

IN PRODUCTION 1985

*Steyr AUG Para*

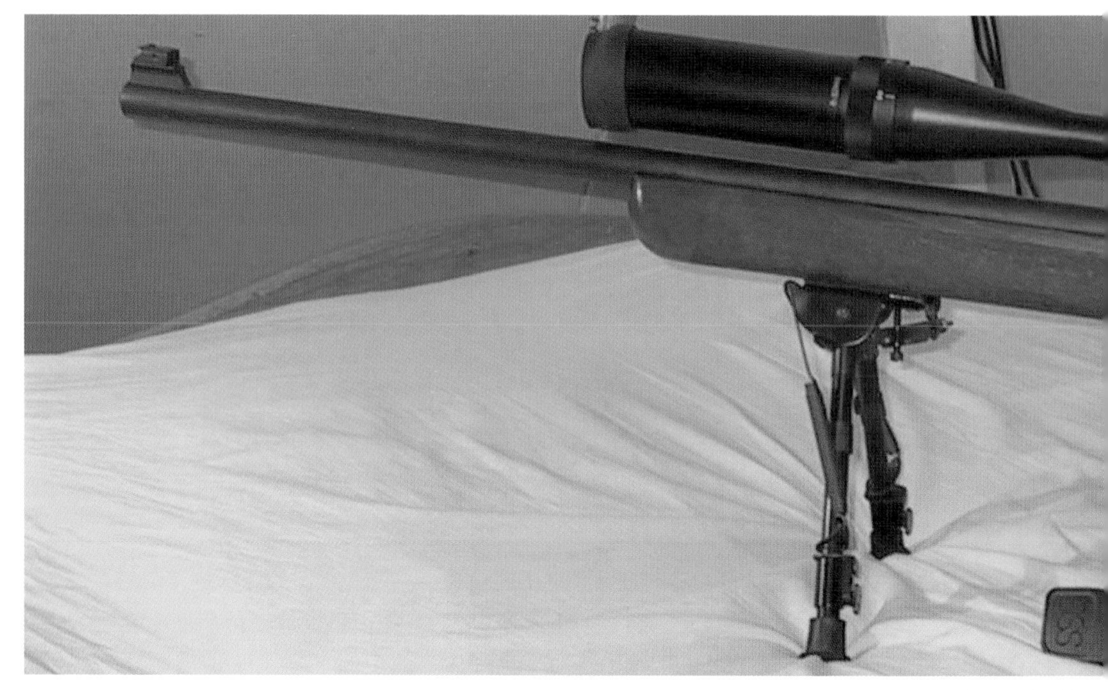

*Steyr SSG*

## STERLING

The Sterling has been used by some 50 or more countries, it is the Canadian Cl, and forms the basis of the Australian Fl submachine gun, and although Sterling collapsed in 1988 the gun is still made under license in India. There is a silenced version, known as the L34 in British service, and also numerous semi-automatic versions of the L2 pattern used by police and security forces around the world.

When the Sten was replaced by the Sterling, it became necessary to replace the Sten Mark 6 silenced version as well, and the L2 Sterling was therefore re-designed into this L34 model, using the silent Sten as a guide but incorporating improvements in technology.

CARTRIDGE
9mm Parabellum

DIMENSIONS
Length, stock extended. 710mm (27.95in)
Length, stock retracted: 480mm {18.90in)
Barrel' 198mm (7.80in)
Weight, empty: 2.70kg(5lb 15oz)
Rifling. 6 grooves, rh
Magazine capacity: 34 rounds
Rate of fire: 550 rds/min

IN PRODUCTION 1953-88

## Steyr 15.2mm IWS2000

The Steyr 15.2mm IWS2000 is a bullpup type anti-materiel rifle in form. It is semi-automatic, and operates on the long recoil system. The barrel is supported in a ring cradle which incorporates a hydro-pneumatic recoil system which, assisted by a high-efficiency muzzle brake, absorbs much of the shock of discharge, making the weapon reasonably comfortable to fire. The IWS2000 strips into two major groups and can easily be carried by a two-man team. There is a bipod and an adjustable monopod under the butt, and a 10x telescope sight is supplied as standard.

The current cartridge is a fin stabilised discarding sabot, tungsten alloy dart weighing 308 grains (20 grammes). Fired at 4757 ft/sec (1450 m/sec) this will completely penetrate 40mm of rolled homogenous steel armour at 1000 metres range, and at this velocity the dart never reaches more than 31 inches above the line of sight; effectively a flat trajectory.

CARTRIDGE
15.2mm APFSDS

DIMENSIONS
Length: 1800mm (70.86in)
Weight: ca 18kg (40lbs)
Barrel- 1200mm (47.24in)
Rifling nil- smoothbore
Magazine- 5 rounds

IN PRODUCTION

*Steyr AUG*

## Steyr AUG Para

This is simply the Steyr AUG assault rifle, converted to 9mm Parabellum calibre by fitting a new barrel, new bolt and a magazine adapter to take the MPi69 magazines. The gas operating system of the rifle is disabled and the AUG Para is a blow back weapon. The long barrel gives it excellent accuracy and a higher velocity than is usual from this cartridge. Steyr were one of the first to adapt an existing assault rifle design to the 9mm cartridge, so producing a submachine gun with the minimum requirement for new parts manufacture, and to date it is the most successful. For some time the company also sold a kit of parts with which any AUG rifle could be converted into the submachine gun version.

CARTRIDGE
9mm Parabellum

DIMENSIONS
Length o/a: 665mm (26.18in)
Barrel: 420mm (16.54in)
Weight, empty: 3.30kg (7lb 4oz)
Rifling:6 grooves, rh
Magazine capacity: 25 or 32 rounds
Rate of fire: 700 rds/min

IN PRODUCTION 1988

## STEYR AUG

This is basically the AUG rifle, but fitted with a heavy barrel and a bipod to act in the light automatic role The barrel it has a muzzle attachment that acts as a flash hider and reduces recoil and muzzle climb during automatic firing. There are two different versions, the HBAR and HBAR/T the former has the carrying handle with built-in optical sight as on the AUG rifle; the latter has a mounting bar on which any sighting telescope or night vision sight can be fitted. Both the HBAR and the HBAR/T can, if required, be further modified to fire from an open bolt; a new hammer assembly is inserted into the butt and a new cocking piece is fitted to the bolt assembly. This modification can be made retrospectively to weapons already issued. Changing to open-bolt firing does not change any of the firing characteristics.

CARTRIDGE
5.56 x 45mm NATO or M193

DIMENSIONS
Length o/a: 900mm (35.43in)
Weight: 490kg (10lb 12oz)
Barrel: 621 mm (24.45in),
Rifling: 6 grooves, rh
Magazine capacity: 30 or 42 rounds
Rate of fire: 680 rds/min

IN PRODUCTION 1980

*M60E3 Machine Gun*

## Steyr MPi69

The Steyr Mpi69 was adopted by the Austrian Army in 1969 and remains in wide use by several other countries and security forces. An excellent weapon its only peculiarity is the attachment of the sling to the cocking system although the Steyr company also makes the MPi81, which is the same weapon but with a conventional cocking handle and with the rate of fire increased to about 700 rds/min. There is also a special long-barrel version of the MPi81, designed for firing out of the ports of an armoured personnel carrier and known as the Loop Hole model.

CARTRIDGE
9mm Parabellum

DIMENSIONS
Length stock extended: 670mm (26.38in)
Length stock folded: 465mm (18.31in)
Barrel: 260mm (10.24in)
Weight, empty: 3.13kg (6lb 14oz)
Rifling: 6 grooves, rh
Magazine capacity: 25 or 32 rounds
Rate of fire: 550 rds/min

## Steyr Mannlicher AUG

The Steyr Mannlicher AUG or Armee Universal Gewhr was designed to an Austrian Army specification and was adopted by them in 1979. It is a bullpup design and makes extensive use of synthtic materials. Only the barrel and mechanism are made of steel, and the receiver is aluminium. The magazine is made of tough, translucent plastic enabling the user to see how many rounds are available. Modular in design, the barrel can quickly be removed and changed for a longer or shorter one, the firing mechanism can be removed and changed for one giving three-round bursts or semi-automatic fire only or any other combination of possibilities; the receiver can be changed to replace the built-in telescope with a mounting platform to which other types of sight can be fitted. It is in service with the armed forces of Ireland, Australia, the Netherlands, several Middle Eastern countries, the US Customs Service, and the Falkland Islands Defence Force. It is made under license in Australia as the F88, and is also fielded by special-forces units all over the world, including the SAS and Germany's GSG-9.

DIMENSIONS
Length o/a: 790mm (31.1in)
Barrel: 508mm (20.0in)
Weight: 3.85kg (8lb 8oz)
Rifling- 6 grooves, rh
Magazine capacity' 30 or 42 rounds
Rate of fire- 650 rds/min

IN PRODUCTION 1978-

SAFETY
A push-through safety is fitted into the stock behind the trigger. When pushed from left to right, the rifle is safe. Pushed from right to left, the rifle is ready to fire. Selection of fire is performed by the trigger; a light pull gives single shots, a heavier pull gives automatic fire.

## Steyr Mannlicher SSG69

The Steyr Mannlicher SSG69 was developed as a sniping rifle for the Austrian Army in 1969, it was later put on the commercial market and was also adopted by numerous military and police forces. Minor changes have been made such as a heavier and larger bolt knob. There is a short-barrelled version, and a special 'Police Version' which will accept a silencer, but they all use the same basic mechanism, a turn-bolt locking by lugs on the bolt turning into recesses in the receiver behind the magazine. The SSG69 is half stocked in synthetic material and has a pistol grip butt. The standard magazine is a rotary, Schoenauer type, though for some years a ten-round detachable box was offered as an alternative.

CARTRIDGE
7.62 x 51 mm NATO

DIMENSIONS
Length o/a: 1140mm (44.9in)
Weight: 3.90kg (8lb 9oz)
Barrel: 650mm (25.6in)
Rifling: 4 grooves, rh
Magazine capacity: 5 rounds

IN PRODUCTION 1969-

## Stinger FIM 92A

Developed since the mid-1960s as a replacement for the first generation Redeye, Stinger had a long and troubled development before finally entering service in 1982.

An improved IR seeker gives all-aspect guidance, the wavelength of less than 4.4 microns being matched to an exhaust plume rather than hot metal. This means that whereas Redeye is limited to stern chase. Stinger permits effective attack from all angles. It is also more resistant to counter measures. IFF (identification friend or foe) is incorporated so that the operator does not have to rely on correct visual identification of oncoming supersonic aircraft.

Stinger made its operational debut with the British SAS during the Falklands War and brought down an Argentine Pucara ground attack aircraft on its first firing at San Carlos on 20 May 1982. Subsequently supplied in large numbers to the Afghan Mujhadeen guerrillas, it was credited with dozens of hits on Soviet Mi-24 Hind helicopter gun ships. The US Army took delivery of its first Stinger in 1982 and they now serve in divisional Air Defence Artillery battalions. Each battalion fields 15 or 20 missile teams that are distributed to brigades and task forces. Most divisions have three battalions. A self-propelled version called the Avenger is also in service, and consists of eight ready to fire missiles mounted on a turret in the rear of an HMMWV (Hummer).

Type: Portable air-defence missile.
Dimensions: (Missile) length 60in (152cm); body diameter 2.75in (7cm); span 5.5in (14cm).
Launch weight: 24lb (10.9kg); whole package 35lb (15.8kg).
Propulsion: Atlantic Research dual-thrust solid.
Guidance: Passive IR homing.
Range: In excess of 3.1 miles (5km).
Flight speed: About Mach 2.
Warhead: Smooth-case fragmentation

TFM

## Stoner SR25

This weapon is based on the M16 and is configured to fire the 7.62mm NATO cartridge. It was designed for use as a support weapon for sniper teams, the second man using it for local defence but having a weapon of sufficient accuracy to stand in for the sniper in the event of him or his weapon becoming ineffective. It is certainly designed for accuracy, with a very heavy free-floating barrel and with the bipod attached to the fore-end and the fore-end attached only to the receiver so as not to place any strain on the barrel. The receiver is a flat top design to which the user can apply various attachments, from a carrying handle to the most sophisticated night vision sights. Tests show that this rifle can consistently put all the shots of a group into a 19mm circle at l00m range.

CARTRIDGE
7.62 x 51mm NATO

DIMENSIONS
Length o/a: 1175mm (46.25in)
Weight: 4.88kg (10lb 12oz)
Barrel: 508mm (20.0in)
Rifling: 4 grooves rh
Magazine: 10 or 20 rounds

IN PRODUCTION 1992-

## TOW BGM 71

The TOW (Tube-Launched, Optically-tracked, Wire-guided) missile is the outcome of a programme begun by Hughes Aircraft in 1965 to replace the 106mm recoilless rifle.

In it's basic infantry form the missile is supplied in a sealed tube that is clipped to the launcher. The missile tube is attached to the rear of the launch tube, the target sighted and the round fired. The boost charge pops the missile from the tube, firing through lateral nozzles amidships. The four wings angled at 45° spring open forwards, and the four tail controls flip open rearwards. The optical sensor and processor in the sight generate the guidance commands by continuously measuring the position of a light source in the missile relative to the line of sight. The steering commands are then sent along twin wires, unreeled by the missile in flight. These drive the helium-pressure actuators working the four tail controls in pairs for pitch and yaw. Early-model TOW's made their combat debut in the early-1970s and also saw large-scale service during the 1973 Arab-Israeli War. Most US Army units now field TOW missiles on a variety of platforms, including AH-1 Cobra attack helicopters, Bradley fighting vehicles, Improved TOW vehicles and HUM-VEEs (Hummers). Infantry units use a man-portable version with a tripod mount.

Propulsion: Hercules K41 boost (0.05s) and sustain (1s) motors.
Dimensions: Length 45 to 75in (1,162mm); body diameter 6in (152mm); span (wings extended) 13.5in (343mm).
Launch weight: (BGM- 71 A) 46.11b (20.9kg).
Range: 1,640 to 12,300ft (500 to 3,750m).
Flight speed: 625mph (1,003km/h).
Warhead: (BGM-71A) Picatinny Arsenal 8.61b (3.9kg) shaped charge with 5.31b (2.4kg) explosive.

## TYPE 92 MG

When it came to equipment the Japanese Army was among the most conservative; and its first light machine guns had been manufactured by Hotchkiss. As a result, most of their machine guns were based on Hotchkiss designs. The Model 92's parentage is strongly apparent from its appearance, but various small changes were made internally by Nambu that, unfortunately, resulted in a weapon that was not as good as an untouched Hotchkiss would have been. The Model 92 was developed from the Taisho 3 Model of 1914, which in its turn was a copy of the French Model 1914 Hotchkiss. The Taisho 3 barrel was more prominently finned, and was fitted with spade grip type triggers, but the main difference was a slight change in the connection between the gas piston and the breech block. This was made to give efficient operation with the lower-powered Japanese 6.5mm cartridge, and because of this alteration the extraction was violent and the cartridges had to be oiled before loading, with all the attendant fouling problems that implied.

Calibre 7.7mm
length 45.5in
Weight 61lb
Barrel 29.5in long, 4 grooves, right hand twist
Feed system 30-round strip
System of operation
Gas; vertical sliding lock
Rate of fire (cyclic) 450rpm
Manufacturers
Nambu Armament Mfg. Co. Tokyo
State Arsenals

## TYPE 96 MG

This weapon was introduced in 1936 (year 2596 in the Japanese calendar, hence Type 96) with the intention of replacing the Taisho 11 model.
Although still based on the same action as the Taisho 11,a number of ideas had been taken from the Czechoslovakian ZB designs, probably from guns captured from the Chinese. The most important feature was that the complicated hopper feed of the Taisho 11 was replaced by a more usual form of top-mounted detachable box magazine; unfortunately this did not do away with the troubles due to the full power rifle round, and the reduced charge cartridge was still necessary.
The offset butt and sights were abandoned in favour of a more conventional form of butt and a drum-set rear sight copied from the ZB design. The quick-change barrel was heavily ribbed throughout its length and, somewhat incongruously, a bayonet boss on the gas cylinder allowed a large sword bayonet to be attached. Another change from the Taisho 11 was the removal of the cartridge oiling system. But since the action was the same, the rounds still required lubrication and this was now done by a combination oiler and magazine loading tool; if anything, this led to a worse state of affairs, since the gun team now carried magazines full of oily cartridges which attracted dust and grit. It is no coincedence that the gun handbook lists 26 different types of stoppage or malfunction as being likely.
In the event the production of the Type 96 never kept up with demand so that it never completely replaced the Taisho 11.

Calibre 6.5mm
Length 41.5in
Weight 20Ib
Barrel 21.7in long, 4 grooves, right hand twist
Feed system 30-round detachable box
System of operation
Gas; rising lock
Rate of fire (cyclic) 550rpm
Manufacturer State Arsenals

*AK 47*

## Type 97 20mm Anti-tank Rifle

In the early 1930s the Japanese Army bought a number of Oerlikon, Solothurn and Hispano weapons for evaluation, and from a study of these came the Type 97, introduced in 1937. It was a heavy and complicated design, but it was undoubtedly capable of dealing with the lighter type of tank which the Japanese anticipated meeting in their Chinese and Manchurian campaigns.

In order to transport the weapon it was provided with attachments beneath the butt and under the cradle to which carrying handles could be fitted to allow it to be carried by four men. A shield was also provided, and with handles and shield in place the total weight was 150lbs. An unusual feature of this weapon was its ability to fire in the automatic mode as a cannon or heavy machine gun; the rate of fire is not known but it is estimated to have been about 350-400rpm.

There are very few reports of this weapon's appearance during World War II; it appears to have been used once or twice in the actions in Malaya and Singapore and to have made a brief appearance in the Southwest Pacific area, but its performance was relatively poor and it was soon outclassed by tank development. There are some reports of it having been used as a beach defence weapon on some of the islands of the Pacific, used to shoot at incoming landing craft; but very few specimens were captured.

Calibre 20mm
Length 82.25in
Weight 115lb
BarreI 41.875in long, 8 grooves, right hand twist
System of operation Gas & blow back, tipping bolt, selective fire
Muzzle velocity 2640ft / sec
Penetration 12mm / 200m / 0 degrees
Manufacturer State Arsenals

## Type 99

After using 6.5mm ammunition since 1897, the Japanese Army decided in 1932 as part of their program to expand their East Asian empire in China and Manchuria to change to something more powerful, and after studying various types developed a 7.7mm round. For some reason this was produced in three versions, one rimmed and interchangeable with British .303, one rimless, and one semi-rimmed. It remains unclear why this was done, since it undoubtedly created serious logistical problems.

The Type 99 machine gun used the rimless 7. 7mm round and was introduced in 1939 with the new ammunition, the rimmed and semi-rimmed types having been put into service in 1932. It was intended to issue the weapon in place of the Models 11 and 96, but production never approached demand and all three guns remained in service, the Type 99 only appearing in relatively small numbers.

Its appearance is virtually the same as the Type 96, since it was little more than 96 in a new calibre. But some internal changes were made, the most important being that at last the need for adequate primary extraction had been appreciated, and the breech was designed to give a slow initial opening movement, and at long last the Japanese Army had a machine gun which did not need to have its cartridges oiled. As a result it was one of the most reliable weapons they ever produced.

Calibre 7.7mm
Length 42.0in
Weight 20Ib
Barrel 21.66in long, 4 grooves, right hand twist
Feed system
30-round detachable box
System of operation Gas; rising lock Rate of fire (cyclic) 800rpm Manufacturer State Arsenals

## UK 2 INCH MORTAR

Developed during the early 1930s the British 2 inch mortar was based on the Spanish 5cm model made by Esperanza & Cie of Vizcaya.
In its original form it did not fully meet British requirements, and it took several years before the Armament Research Department finally perfected the 2in mortar. Its trials were so successful that the Director of Artillery, in view of the threatening international situation in 1938, immediately ordered it into production without the usual exhaustive user trials on preproduction models.
As a result the weapon was in service in numbers when the war broke out when Germany attacked Poland in 1939.
As originally issued, it was a relatively luxurious weapon, with a large base plate, a trip firing mechanism, and a collimating sight with elevating and cross-level bubbles. However, wartime experience soon showed that much of the refinement could be dropped; eventually the base plate shrank to a small curved plate, and the sight was rarely seen, aiming being done by a white line painted on the barrel to give direction and the firer relying on his experience to estimate the elevation.

Calibre 2.0in
Barrel 21in long, smoothbore
Weight in action 19lb (large base plate); 10.5lb (small base plate)
Firing mechanism Trip
Elevation 45-90 degrees
Traverse
Projectiles & weight HE 21lb; Smoke 2lb; Illuminating 1lb 5oz
Maximum range 500yds
Rate of fire 8rpm

## UK 3 INCH MORTAR

The 3in mortar was a development of the Stokes 3in mortar of World War I. It fired a fin-stabilized bomb by means of a charge consisting of a primary cartridge in the tail unit and four secondary cartridges, celluloid tubes containing smokeless powder, tucked between the tail fins and retained by a wire spring The breech end of the mortar rested on a base plate, and the muzzle end was supported by a bipod with a screw elevating and traversing arrangements. To reduce the effect of firing shock on the mounting, the barrel was free to slide in the yoke of the bipod and was controlled by two tension springs clipped to a barrel band. As originally developed the mortar had a maximum range of 1600 yards but, inevitably, the army were soon asking for more range. By adopting a slightly heavier barrel of stronger steel and a stronger base plate it was found possible to adopt a six charge secondary propelling charge which sent the bomb to 2800 yards, and this Mark 2 model became standard.

Much experimental work was done during the war in an endeavour to obtain even greater range; a barrel in 40-ton steel was developed but with the extra propelling charge necessary to reach the target of 4000 yards, this barrel began to bulge. A fresh design in 50-ton steel was then made, and this withstood firings but the accuracy was far below the standard the users were willing to accept.

Calibre 3in
Barrel 51in long, smoothbore Weight
Barrel 44lb
Bipod 45lb
Base plate 37lb In action 112lb
Firing mechanism Drop, fixed striker
Elevation 45-80 degrees
Traverse 5.5 degrees right or left
Projectiles & weight HE 10lb; Smoke 10lb
Maximum range 1600yds (Mk1); 2800yds (Mk2)
Rate of fire 10rpm

*Sten MK2*

## UK Sten, Marks 1-5

In the summer of 1940 the British Government began to look seriously at the question of supplying the British armed forces with a sub-machine gun. Initially it was decided to produce a copy of the German MP28, known as the Lanchester, an order for 50,000 weapons being contemplated. However in January 1941a simplified weapon, designated the N.O.T. 40/1; designed by Major R. V. Shepherd and Mr. H. J. Turpin of the Chief Superintendent of Design's department, was demonstrated at the Royal Small Arms Factory at Enfield Lock. Testing showed the new design to be more than satisfactory. Arrangements were made to organize production and the first weapons began to come from the factories in June 1941. The result of all this effort was the Sten Mark I. While it was a simple weapon, it still had a certain amount of refinement; there was a wooden fore-end and a folding grip for the forward hand, a barrel jacket and protectors for the foresight, and a flash hider-cum-muzzle compensator. A safety slot at the rear of the cocking handle slot allowed the lever to be turned down and locked as a rudimentary safety measure.

The Sten was a highly successful weapon; its introduction was greeted with some reserve by soldiers who were accustomed to more highly finished products, but its performance in battle showed that looks count for little, and the initial misgivings soon died away. It was not without its defects, but it was one of the most effective sub-machine guns of the entire war.

Calibre 9 mm
Length 30.0in
Weight 61b 100z
Barrel 7. 75in long, 2 or 6 grooves, right hand twist
Feed system 32-round detachable box magazine
System of operation Blow back, selective fire
Rate of fire (cyclic) 550rpm
Manufacturers Royal Ordnance Factory, Fazakerley
Birmingham Small Arms Co., Tyseley
Long Branch Arsenal, Ontario, Canada

*Sten MK5*

## US M224 Light Mortar

Designed to replace 81mm (32in) Mortar M29 in US Army service, the 60-mm M224 Lightweight Company Mortar is the product of a lengthy and involved development programme. It has been issued to infantry, air-borne and air-mobile infantry units, and is a long-barrelled weapon that can be fitted with either a conventional bipod or a simple base-plate for use in the 'commando' configuration. Much use is made of aluminium alloys for components such as the large base-plate, and the entire weapon can be broken down into two loads for man-pack transport It is also possible to mount the weapon on some vehicles The main elements of the M224 are the 6.53 kg (14.4 lb) M225 cannon assembly, 6.9 kg (15.2 lb) M170 bipod assembly, 6.53 lb (14.4 lb) M14 base-plate assembly, and 1.63 kg (3.6 lb) M8 auxiliary base-plate, to which must be added to items such as the M64 sight unit. The M224 has a maximum rate of fire of 30 rounds per minute and a sustained rate of fire of 20 rounds per minute.

Perhaps the most important design feature of the M224 is the ammunition it fires, and especially the multi-option fuse involved The M224 fires HE illuminating, smoke and practice rounds, and the multi-option fuse is known as the M734. This is an electronic unit, and was among the first of its type to reach service The M734 has four detonating options high air-burst low air-burst, point detonation and delay. In air burst mode, the number of fragments spread over a wide area comes close to the destructive and anti-personnel effects of 81-mm bombs.

To go with the M224 and its electronically fused bombs, the US Army uses a laser rangefinder to determine target ranges with great accuracy and so allow the first bombs to arrive right on target for maximum effect.

Calibre: 60mm (2.36-in)
Length: 1106 mm (40 in)
Weight: 21.11kg (46.5lb)
Maximum range: 3475m (3800yds)

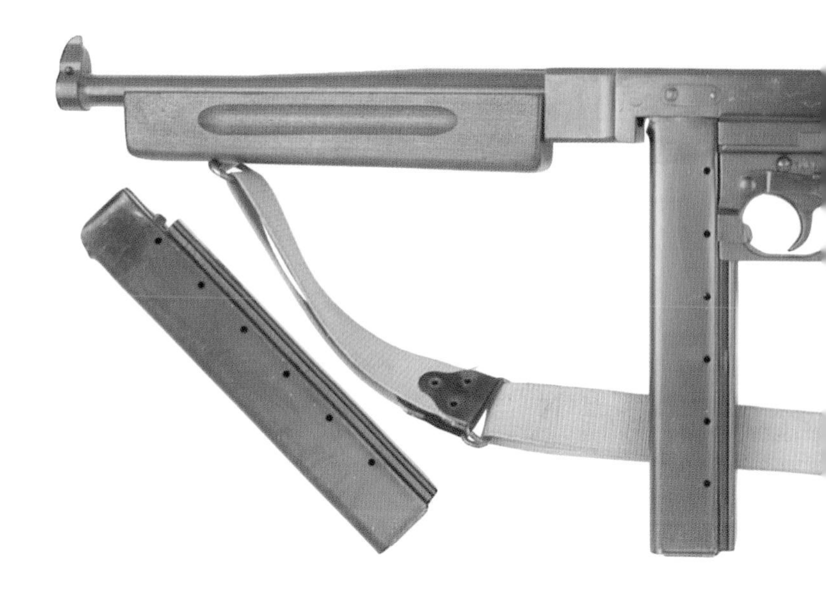

*US Thompson SMG*

## US Mortar, 60mm M2

During the course of World War I the US Army adopted a variety of British and French mortars and rifle grenades, none of which was completely satisfactory. In the 1920s research began to find a more suitable light mortar. The weapon selected was the French 60mm mortar designed by the Edgar Brandt company, and to all intents and purposes it was no more than a scaled-down model of their 81mm model. After evaluation of a number supplied by Brandt, a licence to manufacture was obtained and the drawings modified to United States standards, after which manufacture began in the USA. The weapon, while similar in tactical use to the British 2in, is heavier and more complex. It consists of barrel, breech cap and fixed firing pin, while the Mount M2 comprises base plate and bipod with traversing and elevating mechanisms. Sighting was by the 'Sight, Collimator M4' which carried deflection and elevation scales and was mounted on a special bracket on the mount traversing head. The ammunition provided included the high explosive shell M49A2 of 2.94lbs, a practice shell M50A2 similar to the HE shell but containing only a small charge of gunpowder to give a smoke puff on impact, and an illuminating shell M83 . This carried a 100,000 candle-power star unit suspended from a parachute, and gave illumination for 25 seconds while falling to the ground. This shell was used in considerable numbers to provide battlefield illumination at night so that machine guns and other squad weapons could see their targets. The mortar was also issued to anti-tank gun detachments for the same purpose.

Calibre 60mm
Barrel 28.6in long, smoothbore
Weight
Barrel12.8Ib
Bipod 16.4lb
Base plate 12.8lb
In action 42lb
Firing mechanism Drop, fixed striker
Elevation 40-85 degrees
Traverse 3! degrees right or left
Projectiles & weight HE 2.94lb
Maximum range 1985yds
Rite of fire 18rpm

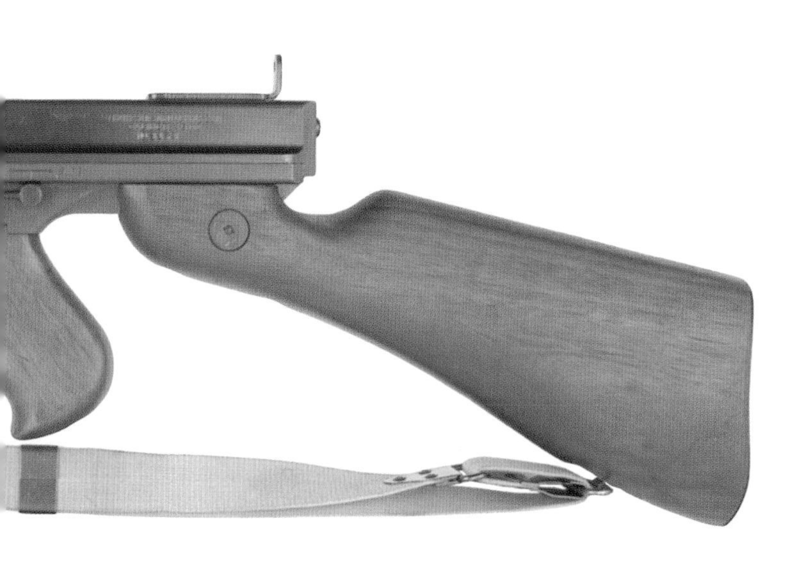

## US Mortar, 81 mm M1

The United States Army adopted the Stokes 3in mortar in 1918 and retained numbers of them after the war ended. In 1920 work began to improve the Stokes design, with particular emphasis on improving the accuracy of the finned bomb. While this work was in progress the French company of Edgar Brandt had developed an 81mm mortar based on Stokes' design, and they offered this model to the US War Department for test. As it appeared to meet the specifications stated by the Army, a number were purchased for evaluation. Subsequent tests proving successful, the manufacturing rights were purchased from Brandt and the weapon entered US service in the early 1930s.

It was originally provided with two high explosive bombs, a 'light' and a 'heavy'. The heavy bomb was fitted with spring loaded fins of greater calibre than the bomb, thus they were well out into the air stream to give the bomb excellent stability. While theoretically very sound-indeed, it was found in practice that the springs tended to lose their tension in storage and the cartridge explosion often bent or warped the fins, leading to unstable or inaccurate flight. As a result this bomb, the M45, was declared obsolete in March 1940 and replaced by the M56 model of the same weight and general appearance but with a cluster of conventional fins.

Calibre 81mm
Barrel 49.5in long, smoothbore
Weight
Barrel 44.5Ib
Bipod 46.5Ib
Base plate 45Ib
In action 136lb
Firing mechanism Drop, fixed striker
Elevation 40-85 degrees
Traverse 5 degrees right or left
Projectiles & weight HE M43 6.87Ib; HE M36 10.62lb; Smoke M57 10.75lb
Maximum range 3290yds (HE M43); 2558yds (HE M36); 2470yds (Smoke)
Rate of fire 18rpm

*Carbine 30cal*

## US CARBINE, CAL .30 M1

The US Carbine M1 originated in 1938 with a request from the infantry for a light rifle, comparable with the 19th century carbine, which could replace the standard rifle and the pistol in arming drivers, machine-gunners, mortar squads, cooks, clerks, and others whose primary function was not rifle-shooting but who, in emergency, might need a weapon with a better reach than the pistol. The request was initially turned down, but was revived in 1940 and this time met with a more favorable reception, since the Army was now expanding and the production of standard rifles was stretched to its utmost. By October 1940 a draft specification had been prepared and circulated to numerous gunmakers, and a specification was issued to the Winchester company to develop a special round of ammunition, using a 110-grain bullet and giving a velocity of 1860 feet per second. This was officially called the '.30 Short Rifle Cartridge' and was largely based on a much older commercial round, the Winchester .32 Automatic sporting rifle cartridge. Seven competing prototype carbines were subjected to trial. The Winchester design was selected for adoption and was standardized as the Carbine M1 late in 1941.

Calibre.30in
Length 36.0in
Weight 5.0lb
Barrel18.0in long, 4 grooves, right hand twist
Feed system 15-round detachable box magazine
System of operation Gas; rotating bolt
Manufacturers:
Inland Mfg. Division of General Motors, Dayton, Ohio
Winchester Repeating Arms Co., New Haven,Conn.
Saginaw Steering Gear Div. of General Motors, Grand Rapids, Michigan
Underwood-Elliot-Fisher, Hartford, Conn .
Rochester Defense Corp. , Rochester, NY.
QuaIity Hardware Corp., Chicago, III.
Rock-Ola Corp., Chicago, III.
National Postal Meter Corp . , Rochester, NY.
Standard Products Co., Port Clinton, Ohio
Intemational Business Machines Corp., Poughkeepsie, NY.

## US RIFLE, CAL .30 M1 (GARAND)

John C. Garand first produced a repeating rifle for trial in 1920, but it was not until later that he joined the design staff of Springfield Arsenal and went on to develop the rifle which will always be associated with his name. In 1929 a series of tests of competing designs of rifle were held at Aberdeen Proving Ground, as a result of which a Garand design of gas-operated rifle was selected as the most promising. Further development took place, and in 1936 it was standardized as the US Rifle M1.

The operation is by gas tapped very close to the muzzle end of the barrel, driving a long-stroke piston backwards. This, by means of a cam, rotates and opens the bolt and cocks the firing hammer. The return spring is carried in the gas piston, an arrangement which keeps the action body short and compact. Feed is from a magazine loaded by an eight-round clip, when the last round is fired the clip is ejected and the action is held open for re-loading. This is probably the least desirable feature of the Garand, since single rounds cannot be loaded to 'top up' the magazine; it has to be a full clip or nothing. It also led to a tactical disadvantage in that the ejected clip made a most distinctive noise if it fell on hard ground, thus alerting the enemy to the fact that the rifleman was now holding an empty rifle. But in spite of this small defect, the Garand proved reliable and accurate in service all over the world. US rifle, cat .30 M1 (Garand)

Caliber .30in
Length 43.0in
Weight 91b 8oz
Barrel 24.0in long, 4 grooves, right hand twist
Feed system 8-round integral magazine, clip-loaded
System of operation Gas piston, turning bolt
Manufacturers Springfield Arsenal. Winchester Repeating Arms Go., New Haven, Gonn., USA

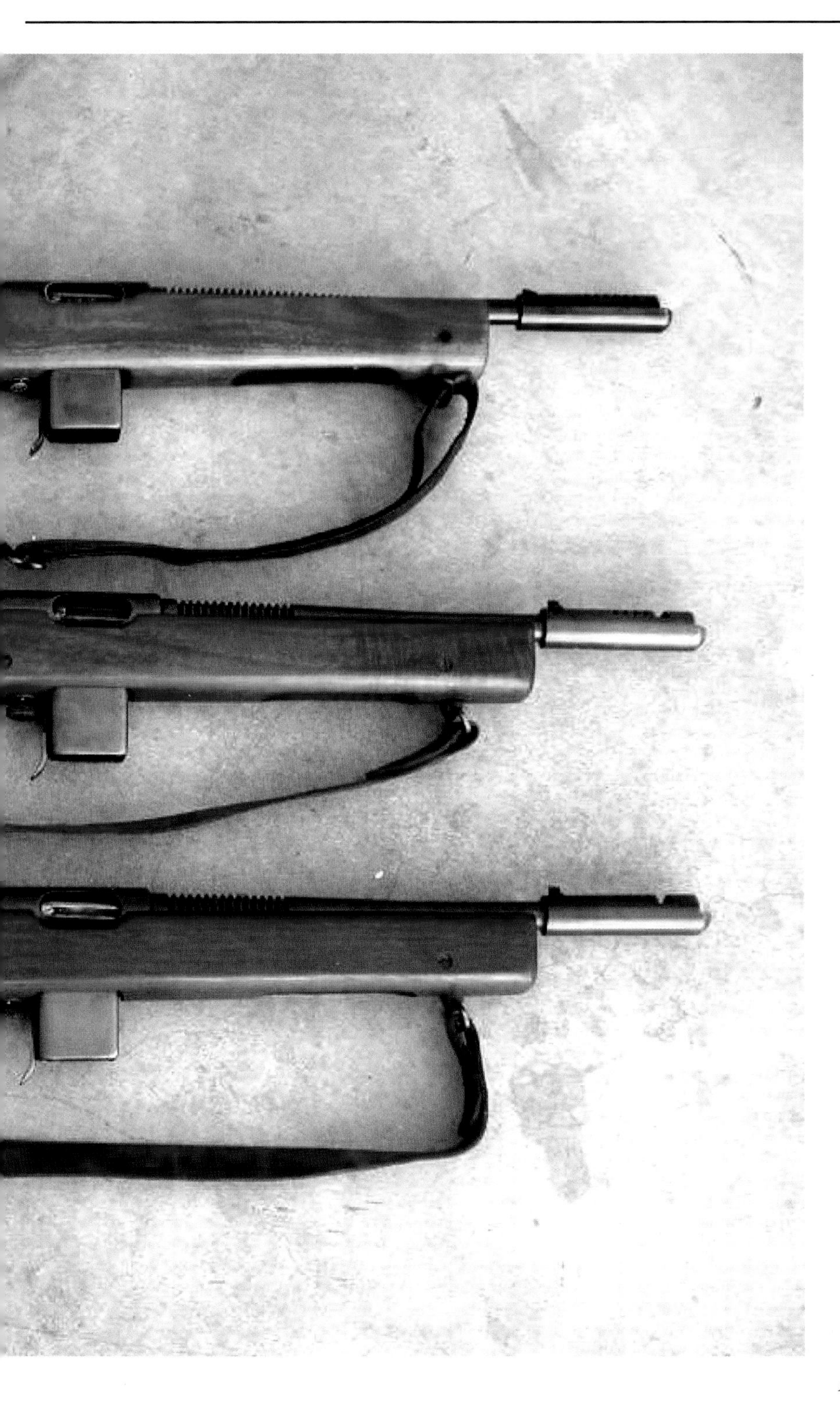

*Reising SMG*

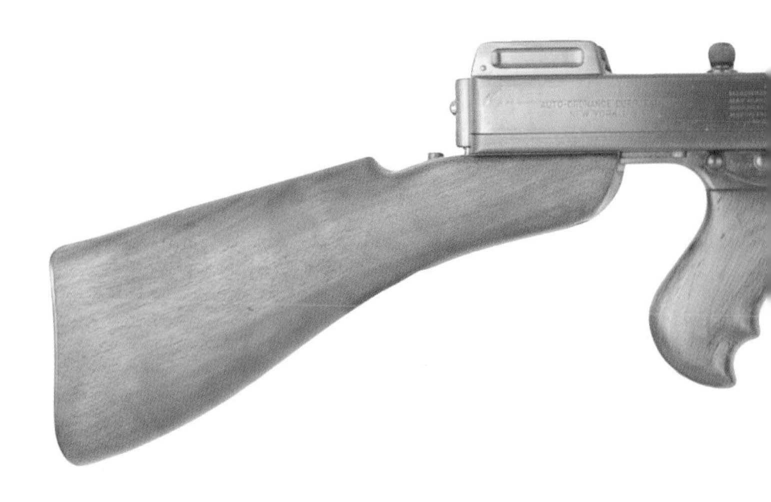

*Thompson M1921*

## USA Reising sub-machine gun

This weapon was designed by a Mr. Eugene Reising and patented in June 1940. After testing by various authorities it was put into production, and a quantity estimated to be in the region of 100,000 of this and the similar Model 55 variant were produced before manufacture ceased in 1945.

The Reising was a rather unusual weapon in that it fired from a closed bolt at all times and the bolt was locked to the receiver before the round was fired. Upon firing the recoil of the cartridge case forced the bolt back, but opening was delayed while the bolt was unlocked and lowered by cams working in paths in the gun body. The bolt then recoiled in the usual way, returning under spring pressure to chamber a fresh round and then being cammed back into the locked position. A hammer was then released to strike the firing pin and fire the next round.

One might justifiably expect trouble from overheating and cook-offs of rounds in the chamber, but there do not appear to have been any complaints on that score. However there were complaints about other defects, principally of jamming andl failure of the bolt to lock when the weapon was dirty, lack of interchangeability of parts and weakness of the springs.

The greater part of the production of the Reising sub-machine gun was taken by the United States Marine Corps and it was extensively used by them in the campaigns in the South Pacific. A small number of weapons was also purchased by the British Government for issue to the Canadian Army and for supply to the Soviet Government.

Calibre O.45in
Length 35.75in
Weight 61b 12oz
Barrel 11in long, 6 grooves, right hand twist
Feed system 12 or 2Q-round detachable box magazine
System of operation Retarded blow back
Rate of fire (cyclic) 550rpm
Manufacturer Harrington & Richardson Arms Co. , Worcester, Mass.

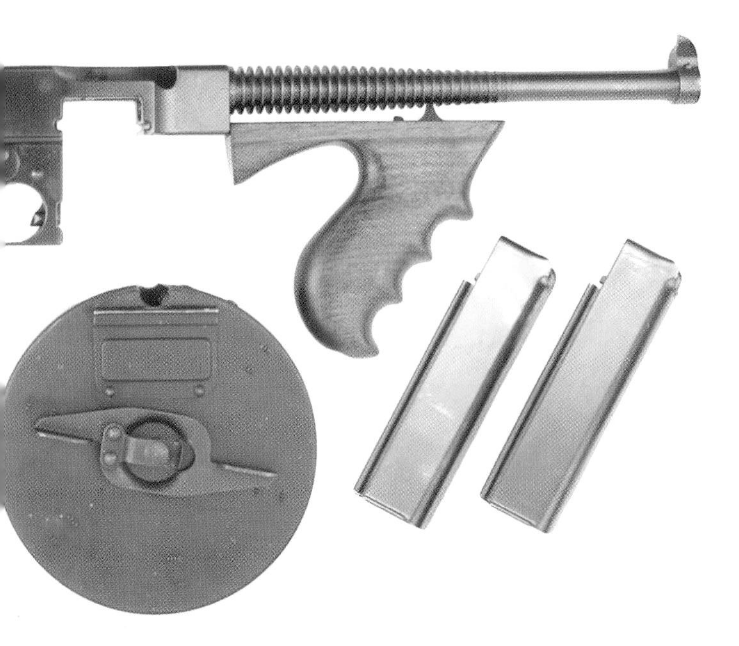

## USA Thompson sub-machine gun

The Auto-Ordnance Corporation was founded in America in 1916 with the intention of developing a variety of weapons but will forever be associated with just one, the Thompson sub-machine gun. Named for General John T. Thompson, the company's design director , the first models were built in prototype form in 1919. The first production models appeared in 1921 and from then on manufacture was small but continuous through-out the 1920s and 1930s. The first official military recognition came when the United States Marine Corps were issued with a number of the 1927 model, which were officially named the M1928.

In 1939 the Thompson was the only sub-machine gun in production outside Europe, and as a result the government of Britain, France and Sweden hurriedly placed orders. Shortly afterwards the US Army also ordered a large quantity. But the Thompson was a difficult gun to manufacture; the engineering processes were numerous and complicated and the materials used were of the best quality, a fact which was reflected in the price-almost £50. By the end of 1940 orders for over 318,000 guns had been placed; previous production had been by the Colt Company under license from the Auto-Ordnance Corporation, but now Auto-Ordnance built their own factory and by late summer of 1941 were producing guns. The Savage Arms Co. were also given a license to manufacture, and between these two plants over one and a quarter million Thompson guns were produced during the war.

Calibre .45in
Length 33.25in
Weight 10lb 2oz
Barrel10.5in long, 6 grooves, right hand twist
Feed system 20 or 30 round detachable box magazine, or 50 or 100-round detachable drum magazine
System of operation Delayed blow back, selective fire
Rate of fire (cyclic) 800rpm
Manufacturers
Colts Patent Firearms Co.
Savage Arms Co.

*SMG M3*

## USA SUB-MACHINE GUN, M3

When the United States entered the war the only sub-machine gun available was the Thompson, this was not well suited to mass production and there existed no viable alternative. In October 1942 a completely new design was inaugurated by the Small Arms Development Branch of the US Ordnance Corps Technical Division, and right from the start the importance of simplicity of production was well to the forefront. The first prototype, the Machine Pistol T15 was capable of single shot or automatic fire, but the single shot facility was dropped to turn it into the T20. This was tested in Late November 1942 and found favour in the eyes of potential users, so that on Christmas Eve 1942 it was formally approved as the Sub-machine gun M3.

The design was relatively simple, and from its shape it came to be called 'The Grease Gun'. The barrel projects from the front cap of a cylindrical body, the ejection port is covered by a hinged flap, the pistol grip is, as the rest of the weapon, of steel, and a simple collapsible wire stock is fitted. Cocking was performed by a crank on the right side and was one of the less successful features; another was the design of single-column magazine which inevitably gave stoppages and misfeeds throughout the gun's life. Despite these minor faults, the M3 did what it set out to do; provide a cheap and efficient weapon which could be stamped out by the thousand in a short time, over 606,000 being produced.

Calibre .45in (or 9mm-see text)
Length 30in
Weight 8lb 15oz
Barrel 8.0in long, 4 grooves, right hand twist
Feed system 30-round detachable box magazine
System of operation Blow back
Rate of fire (cyclic) 450rpm
Manufacturer Guide Lamp Division of General Motors, Anderson, Indiana, USA

## USSR 5CM MORTARS, M1940 & M1941

The M1940 5cm Mortar was developed from, and soon replaced, the earlier Model 1938 and Model 1939. Incorporating all the lessons learnt from the preceding designs the M1940 was of fairly conventional in appearance, using a small base plate, barrel, and pressed-steel bipod with elevating and traversing screws, but in addition it had a small recoil buffer between the barrel and the bipod yoke, a refinement hardly necessary in such a small weapon. The most interesting technical feature was the system of controlling range. Although the elevation gear allowed setting of any elevation between 45 and 75 degrees, the sights were arranged so that the mortar could only be fired at these two angles, and control of range at each elevation was done by venting a proportion of the propellant gas to the atmosphere, thus reducing the amount available to propel the bomb. The firing pin holder was constructed to act as a spring loaded poppet valve, the amount of opening of which could be governed by a setting sleeve.

While the 1940 was quite efficient, it was still capable of simplification in the interests of faster production and easier handling, and it was replaced in the following year by the M1941. This dispensed with the bipod and buffer and hinged the barrel to the base plate. The sights were simplified and the gas system changed to vent through an exhaust pipe below the barrel. The same method of firing at fixed elevations was retained.

Calibre 5cm
Barrel 21.0in long
Weight in action 21.3lb
Firing Mechanism DropElevation fixed 45 or 75 degrees
Traverse both models; 9° at 45°
Projectile & weight HE 1.5lb
Maximum range 800m
Rate of fire 30rpm

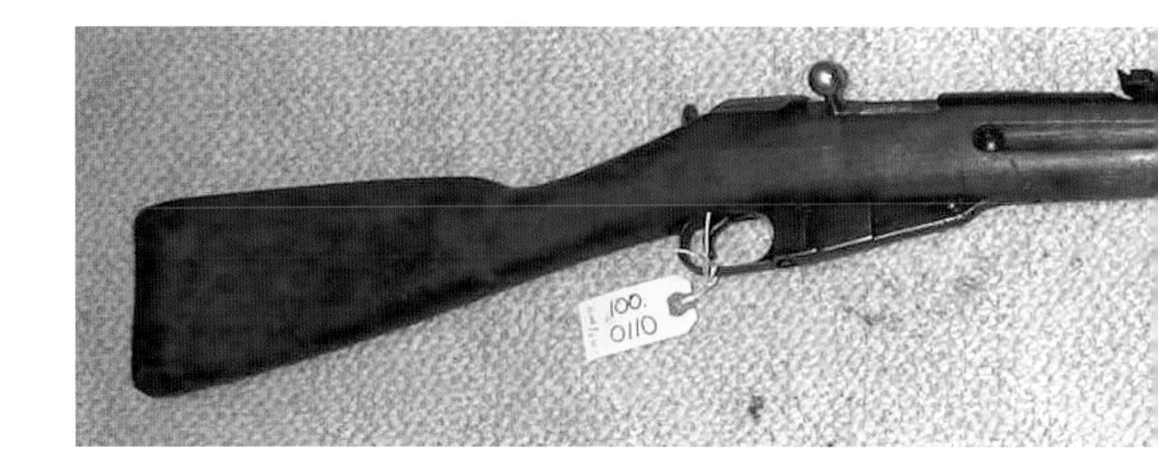


*Mosin-Nagant M1891: 30 rifle*

## 82MM MORTAR, M41:43

As with the 5cm model, the Soviet infantry were presented with a rapid succession of 82mm mortars, the Models 1936, 1937 and 1941. The first two were quite orthodox, using the usual base plate and bipod configuration. However huge numbers of all types of weapons were lost to the advancing German army in 1941 and a new simplified design was introduced that could be rapidly produced in the huge numbers necessary to make good Russia's losses. The 1941 model replaced all the others and carried the mass production theme even further. The base plate was a circular steel stamping, and the twin spring buffers of the 1937 model were replaced by a much simpler single spring pattern contained in a tube beneath the barrel. But the greatest change was in the bipod assembly. Previous designs, indeed all designs based on the normal barrel-bipod-baseplate layout, required that either the three components be carried individually by man power or that they be carried in some form of vehicle. The designers of this mortar, however, adopted a novel solution and formed small stub axles on the lower ends of the bipod legs, onto which small pressed-steel wheels could be fitted, the incorporation of wheels allowed the weapon to be moved quickly, in one piece, ready to fire, as the crew could simply pull it behind them. Once in action the wheels were removed to allow the bipod feet to dig into the ground. This design was eventually refined by designing the lower section of the bipod so that the wheels remained permanently attached, being so located that they were clear of the ground when the mortar was in action.

Calibre 82mm
Barrel 48in long, smoothbore
Weight
Barrel 42.9lb
Bipod & wheels 45.2lb
Base plate 41.9lb
In action 99.2lb
Firing mechanism Drop
Elevation 45-80 degrees
Traverse 3 degrees right or left
Projectile & weight HE 7.4lb
Maximum range 3100m
Rate of fire 15-20rpm

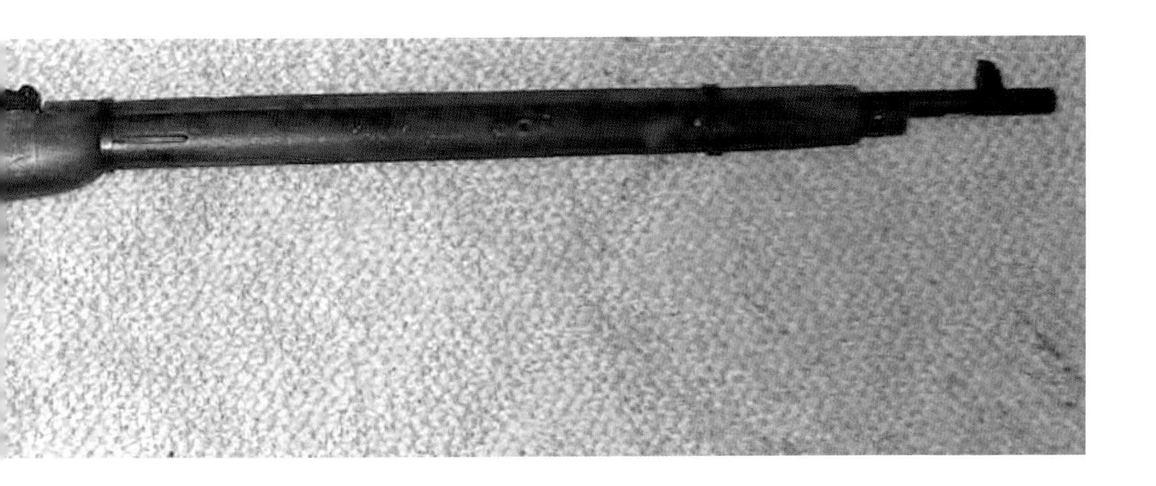

## MOSIN-NAGANT M1891: 30 RIFLE

The Model 1930G (sometimes called the 1891/ 30) is one of a series of rifles based the Mosin-Nagant Model 1891.

The title 'Mosin-Nagant' commemorates the original design, basically that of the Belgian Nagant brothers with modifications due to Colonel S. I. Mosin of the lmperial Russian Army. Its turnbolt action is much the same as any other, though the bolt is, unusually, made in three pieces. A novel feature of the design is the provision of a cartridge control catch. One of the difficult problems of weapon design is the efficient feeding of rimmed cartridges from a magazine; the pressure of the magazine spring tends to jam the rims together and give rise to stoppages. The Mosin-Nagant used a spring-loaded latch, controlled by the operation of the bolt, to hold down the second round in the magazine and thus take pressure off the top round so that it could be easily loaded into the chamber by the closing bolt without the danger of the rim of the second round interfering due to the upward pressure of the spring.

The original 1891 model was a 'long 'rifle, and was always used with its bayonet attached. It was partnered by a slightly shorter weapon, known as the 'Dragoon Rifle', but this was by no means as short and handy as the contemporary carbines in use by other armies. In 1931 the Soviet Army introduced the 1891/ 30 which was more or less the Dragoon Rifle with improved sights and with the design somewhat simplified so as to make production easier. It became the standard infantry rifle and remained so throughout the war , although it was widely supplemented by the later model of carbine and, of course, by the ubiquitous sub-machine guns which were a lot cheaper and quicker to make.

Numbers of the Model 1891/ 30 were fitted with sighting telescopes for use by snipers.

Caliber 7.62mm
Length 48.5in
Weight Bib 11oz
Barrel28.7in long, 4 grooves, right hand twist
Feed system 5-round integral box magazine
System of operation Turn-bolt Manufacturer State Arsenals

*PPS 43*

## PPD 1940

PPD is the abbreviation for 'Pistolet Pulyemet Degtyarev' or Machine Pistol designed by Degtyarev, and the term is qualified by the date, since he designed a number of weapons from 1934 onwards. It is doubtful whether very many were made before 1937, but after they proved their usefulness in the Spanish Civil War, they were selected for quantity production. There were a number of small variations of this model, known as the 1934/ 38, but in 1940 it was redesigned to make it more suitable for mass production. The earlier complicated cooling slots in the barrel jacket were simplified into a few long cuts, and one or two other small changes were made for ease of production.

Like all Soviet sub-machine guns the barrel was internally chromium-plated, a refinement rarely found in weapons of any other country, but one which makes the barrel more resistant to wear and more tolerant of the lack of cleaning that sub-machine guns some-times suffer from in war. The calibre is 7.62mm Soviet Pistol, a cartridge derived from the German 7.63mm Mauser round and is one of the few bottle-necked cartridges used with sub-machine guns. Of smaller calibre than the average sub-machine gun round, it compensates to some degree by having a rather higher velocity than average.

The number of PPD sub-machine guns produced is not known, but it was probably small by Russian standards. Production only lasted from the autumn of 1940 to late 1941, after which it was replaced by the PPSh model, and photographs of it in action are few and far between. While it was a very good weapon, and relatively simple to make, it still was not simple enough for the volume of production the Soviets needed to combat the German advance in 1941-42.

Calibre 7.62mm
Length 31in
Weight 8lb 2oz
Barrel 10.5in long, 4 grooves, right hand twist
Feed system 71-round detachable drum magazine
System of operation Blow back, selective fire
Rate of fire (cyclic) 800rpm
Manufacturer State Arsenals

## PPS-42

This was the third standard sub-machine gun adopted by the Red Army during the war, and was designed by A. I. Sudarev. In view of the Soviet system of selecting one design and mass-producing it to the exclusion of every other, it is unusual to find this weapon being apparently produced at the same time as the PPSh, but this was due to the exigencies of war. When the city of Leningrad was besieged by the German Army in 1941-42, weapons were in short supply, and the PPS was designed and put into production inside the besieged city, being sent straight from the factory to the nearby front line. It was a remarkable production, entirely stamped from steel except for the barrel and bolt, and spot-welded together. The only non-metal parts are the wooden grips and a small piece of leather acting as a buffer for the bolt. Finish is non-existent, rough welds and grinding marks being apparent all over, and it must be the cheapest weapon of any type ever produced. But like most Russian weapons it is rugged, it works well and reliably. Many thousands were turned out, both in its original form (PPS-42) and in a slightly modified form (PPS-43), which is substantially the same.

The perforated barrel jacket extends beyond the muzzle to act as a muzzle brake and compensator, as in the PPSh; a curved box magazine is fitted; and the skeleton steel butt folds across the top of the gun body. A simple safety catch is fitted in the front edge of the trigger guard, and there is no provision for firing single shot.

Calibre 7.62mm
length 32.25in
Weight 7lb 6oz
Barrel10in long, 4 grooves, right hand twist
Feed system 35-round detachable box magazine
System of operation Blow back, automatic only
RIte of fire (cyclic) 700rpm
Manufacturer State Arsenals

## PPSh-1941

The Pistolet Pulyemet Shpagin was developed in 1940-41 as a replacement for the PPD-40 model, since although the PPD was good it was not entirely suited to fast production in huge quantities, which was the Soviet's primary concern in 1941. The PPSh used stamped steel for the body and jacket, although the barrel was still chromium lined and the weapon still used a wooden stock. The entire assembly was by pinning and welding, and the barrel jacket extended beyond the muzzle to act as a muzzle brake and compensator to divert some of the gases upwards and thus counteract the tendency, common with all sub-machine guns, for the muzzle to creep upwards during auto-automatic fire.

The 71-round drum magazine adopted for the PPD was retained, since production of this item was well established and it gave the firer a good reserve of ammunition, no bad thing considering the high rate of fire of this weapon. The mechanism was simple blow back, a bolt with fixed ring pin and a return spring being almost the only components apart from an agriculturally simple firing mechanism. It was robust, simple to use, and cheap to make, and something like five million were made during the war .

The PPSh sub-machine gun came to be almost the badge of the Red soldier, much as the MP38 was that of the German, Whole divisions were armed with nothing else, since it was a weapon which well suited the Soviet tactics and spirit.

Calibre 7.62mm
Length 33.10in
Weight 8lb
Barrel 10.5in long, 4 grooves, right hand twist
Feed system 71-round detachable drum or 35 round detachable box
System of operation Blow back, selective fire
Rate of fire (cyclic) 900rpm
Manufacturer State Arsenals

*USSR Tokarev auto rifle, SVT-40*

## USSR Tokarev auto rifle, SVT-40

The Tokarev SVT 40 was derived from an earlier model, the SVT 38, which was itself derived from an earlier Simanov design. The differences between the SVT40 and the SVT 38 were largely a matter of simplifying production and improving reliability. The Model 40 was issued in, what by Russian terms, were small numbers during the war and can be distinguished from the Model 38 by having more of the barrel exposed, by having a two or three baffle muzzle brake instead of the six baffle pattern of the earlier one, and by using a shorter bayonet. The Model 1938 proved to be fragile in service and was withdrawn in favor of the 1940; this, in turn, suffered from an inability to withstand the rigors of active service unless carefully nursed. It appears that these rifles were generally issued to NCOs of infantry regiments, but were later withdrawn and the majority of them converted to sniping rifles, an application where the self-loading action was advantageous and where the sniper could devote some time to careful maintenance of the weapon. Wartime production of the SVT40 totalled over 1,322,000 rifles with an additional 51,700 sniper models.

Caliber 7.62mm
Length 48.1 in
Weight Bib 8oz
Barrel 24.60in long, 4 grooves, right hand twist
Feed system 10-round detachable box magazine
System of operation Gas; tipping bolt
Manufacturer State Arsenals

*UZI*

## UZI

One of the most famous submachine guns in the world, the Uzi has been made under license in Belgium and Germany, and the general layout and principles of its mechanism have been copied in several countries. It is still in production in Israel, and has been joined in the past decade by two smaller models, the Mini-Uzi and the Micro-Uzi these resemble the Uzi but are simply smaller in all dimensions except the calibre. They are easily identifiable by their similarity with the basic Uzi and by their names, which are marked on the left side of the receiver.

CARTRIDGE
9mm Parabellum

DIMENSIONS
Length, fixed stock: 640mm (25.2in)
Length. stock extended: 640mm (25.2in)
Length. stock retracted: 440mm (173in)
Barrel: 260mm (10.24in)
Weight, empty: 3.50kg (7lb 11oz)
Rifling: 4 grooves, rh
Magazine capacity: 25, 32 or 40 rounds
Rate of fire: 600 rds/min

IN PRODUCTION 1953

*PPSH 1941*

## V-94 ANTI-MATERIAL RIFLE

The V-94 is reminiscent of the WW2 Simonov PTRS anti-tank rifle in appearance. It has a long barrel, prominent muzzle brake, bipod, pistol grip, and a wooden stock. There are no iron sights, as the weapon has a mount for a telescope sight. The mechanism is gas operated, semi-automatic. There is a large locking lever on the receiver to allow the receiver and butt to be disconnected from the barrel, and folded around for compact carrying. The V94 has a muzzle velocity of 2790 ft/sec (850 m/sec).

Cartridge
12.7 x 108mm DShK

DIMENSIONS
Length, in firing position: 66.93in (1700mm)
Length, folded for carrying: 41.30in (1100mm)
Barrel: 40.16in (1020mm)
Weight: 25lb 13oz (11.70kg)
Rifling: 8 grooves, rh
Magazine: 5-round box

IN PRODUCTION 1994-

*VAL Silent Sniper*

## VAL Silent Sniper

This weapon was first revealed in 1994. It is a silent semi-automatic rifle firing a special, heavy 9mm bullet at subsonic velocity. It is claimed that the special cartridge will defeat all levels of body armour protection out to ranges of 400 metres or more; as with all Russian weapons, such claims should be treated with reserve until confirmed independently.

It has a fixed skeleton stock and makes extensive use of synthetic materials in its construction, both factors that contribute to its remarkably light weight.

CARTRIDGE
9 x 39mm special

DIMENSIONS
Length, stock extended: 875mm (34.45in)
Length stock folded- 615mm (2421in)
Weight: 2.50kg (51b 8oz)
Barrel- Not known
Rifling: not known
Magazine capacity- 20 rounds
Rate of fire: not known

IN PRODUCTION 1993-

*Valmet M78*

## Valmet M78

In 1962 Valmet produced the first of what was to become a series of assault rifles based on the Kalashnikov AK weapons. The M1962 differed externally from the Kalashnikov in its perforated plastic fore-end, tube type stock and prominent rear sight although internally it was almost identical. This was followed by the M1971 that reverted to a stock and fore-end design like those of the original Kalashnikov. The M1976 introduced the first major changes with many components being replaced with stamped or pressed steel alternatives to ease production.

The M1978 was essentially a heavy-barrelled model of the M1976 intended as a light squad support weapon. The longer and heavier barrel extends the effective range from the 400m or so of the rifle to 600-700 metres. In 1987 Valmet was merged with Sako and the latest in the line of Valmet rifles was produced as the Sako M90 covered elsewhere.

CARTRIDGE
762 x 39mm Soviet M1943
and others

DIMENSIONS
Length o/a- 1060mm (4173in)
Weight: 470kg (101b 6oz)
Barrel: 480mm (189in)
Rifling- 4 grooves, rh
Magazine capacity- 15 or 30 rounds
Rate of fire- 650 rds/min

IN PRODUCTION 1978-86

## VEKTOR R4

This is the South African army's standard rifle and is a license-produced version of the Israeli Galil with some modifications for South African service use. Changes include manufacturing the butt and fore-end in synthetic materials rather than steel, in consideration of the bush temperatures common in Africa, and lengthening the butt since the average South African soldier was larger than his Israeli counterpart. Other components were strengthened, and a bipod with wire cutting ability was provided. There is also a carbine version, the R5 with a 332mm barrel, and a compact version, the R6, with a 280mm barrel. Semi-automatic versions of all three weapons are produced for use by police and paramilitary forces and for export.

CARTRIDGE
5.56 x 45mm M193

DIMENSIONS
Length: stock extended: 1005mm (39.57in)
Length, stock folded: 740mm (29.13in)
Weight: 430kg (91b 8oz)
Barrel: 460mm (18.1in)
Rifling: 6 grooves, rh
Magazine capacity: 35 rounds
Rate of fire: 700 rds/min

IN PRODUCTION 1982-

## VEKTOR SS77

The SS 77 is an air-cooled, gas-piston operated weapon and uses a breech-block which swings sideways into a recess in the receiver wall to lock. The barrel has a quick-change facility and is externally fluted to save weight and also increase the cooling surface. The gas regulator is adjustable and also has a position that closes the exhaust to give minimal emission of gas allowing the gun to be safely fired in enclosed spaces. There is an adjustable bipod, a combined barrel changing and carrying handle, and a synthetic skeleton stock. In 1994 the Mini-SS kit was introduced to enable the SS77 to be converted to fire 5.56mm ammunition.

CARTRIDGE
7.62 x 51mm

DIMENSIONS
Length, butt extended: 45.47in (1155mm)
Length, butt folded 37.0in (940mm)
Weight unloaded: 21lb 3oz (960kg)
Barrel: 21.65in (550mm)
Rifling: 4 grooves, rh
Feed system: disintegrating or non-disintegrating metal link belt.
Cyclic rate: 800 rds/min

IN PRODUCTION: 1986

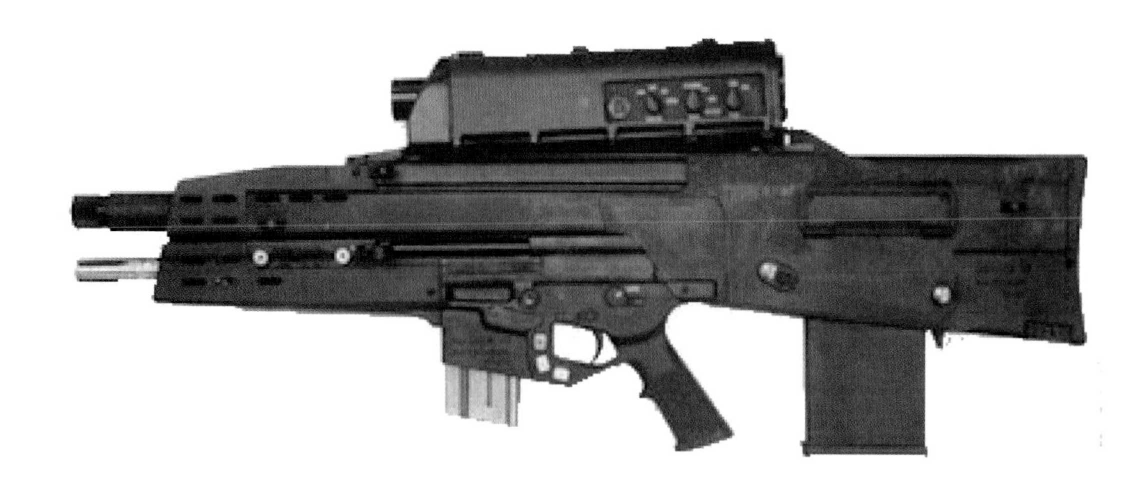

*XM-29 Objective Individual Weapon*

## Vickers Berthier

The Vickers-Berthier machine gun was the invention of a French designer, M. Adolphe PVM Berthier, who patented the essential details as early as 1909. The gun was completed in the early 1920s, and in 1925 the manufacturing rights were purchased by Vickers of England, who there after offered it commercially. The early models were purchased in small numbers by several countries, and in 1933 the Indian Government adopted it as their standard light machine gun. It was also tested in Britain for possible adoption but lost out by a narrow margin to the Bren gun. Indeed the Vickers-Berthier and Bren are very similar in both appearance and operation.

The V-B was to be found with Indian Army divisions throughout the war, though in many cases battle losses were replaced by Bren guns where the logistic situation made this quicker and easier than providing new V-Bs from India. Due to the similarity between the two weapons there seems to have been little problem in retraining the troops.

Vickers-Berthier LMG, Mk3
Calibre .303in
Length 46.5in
Weight 22lb
Barrel 23.5in long, 5 grooves, right hand twist
Feed system 30-round detachable box magazine
System of operation Gas; tipping bolt
Rate of fire (cyclic) 600rpm
Manufacturer Royal Ordnance Factory, Ishapore, India